Machine Age
To
Jet Age

Radiomania's™ Guide to Tabletop Radios
1933-1959
(with market values)

Mark V. Stein

Radiomania™ Publishing
2109 Carterdale Road
Baltimore, Maryland 21209

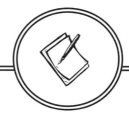

NOTICE

The market values indicated in this reference are based on a number of different sources.
Actual prices will vary dependent on a number of variables.
Neither the author nor the publisher assumes responsibility for losses
which might result from the use of this book.

Published by
Radiomania™ Books
Copyright 1994

Additional copies of this book may be ordered directly from the publisher
by sending $24.95 plus $2.00 shipping and handling by check or money order payable to:

Radiomania™
Department 1ED
2109 Carterdale Road 21209 USA

Future editions of this reference are currently in progress.
If you care to contribute photographs, advertising brochures or other items,
please write the author directly in care of the above address.
All contributed items will be returned upon request and contributors given
due credit in the acknowledgments

Book designed by Jane E. Rubini

DEDICATION

FOR JANE, MY WIFE.
FOR ALL OF HER PATIENCE,
UNDERSTANDING
AND SUPPORT
(NOT TO MENTION ARTISTIC DIRECTION)
THROUGHOUT MY EFFORTS
TO COMPLETE THIS BOOK.
I COULDN'T HAVE DONE IT
WITHOUT HER,
NOR WOULD I HAVE WANTED TO.

Acknowledgements:

This book was realized through
the cooperative efforts of many
collectors. The major contributors
are as follows:

ALAN JESPERSON AND MIKE EMERY
COLLECTORS AND DEALERS, SPECIALIZING IN ZENITH AND E.H. SCOTT
RADIOS. PO BOX 17338, MINNEAPOLIS, MN 55417
(612) 727-2489

STEVEN SANDLER
COLLECTOR OF RADIOS AND OTHER ITEMS OF MACHINE AGE DESIGN.

FITO MIRKIN
COLLECTOR OF HIGH-STYLE BAKELITE, CATALIN AND PLASTIC RADIOS.
6 BARNSTABLE CT., OWINGS MILLS, MD 21117

JOHN ENGLAND
COLLECTOR OF STROMBERG CARLSON RADIOS AND RELATED ITEMS.
P.O. BOX 59136, SCHAUMBERG, IL 60159

BARRY ZIMMERMAN
COLLECTOR OF A WIDE VARIETY OF HIGH-END VINTAGE RADIOS.
5825 WOODWINDS COURT, FREDERICK, MD 21701
(301) 696-5561

REV. MAURICE S. MOORE
COLLECTOR OF ALL TYPES OF VINTAGE RADIOS.
200 W. ALL SAINTS STREET, FREDERICK, MD 21701
(301) 663-3824

AARON MALL
COLLECTOR OF BENDIX RADIOS AND RELATED MEMORABILIA.
903 DROPLEAF COURT, BALTIMORE, MD 21208

IN ADDITION TO THE ABOVE, THE FOLLOWING INDIVIDUALS HAVE ALSO
CONTRIBUTED TO THE COMPLETION OF THIS BOOK.

SPENCER DOGGETT, ROBERT PRINCE, IRA GROSSMAN, THOMAS SELLER, TED'S
VINTAGE RADIO, MARK ALZAPIEDI, STEWART STRUZER, STAN ROSENSTEIN, JAY
KIESSLING, BOB KAMINSKY, JOEL HALSER, PHIL HARRIS, MARION VAN HILL, JOE
GREENBAUM, DAVID GILLIS, JOHNNY JOHNSON, SID STIVLAND, FRANK MOORE,
MARTIN BERGAN, BOB PEKLO, BARNEY VAN HORN, JAY MALKIN,
GEORGE BRECKENRIDGE, LARRY STENCEL, GEORGE KACZOWKA, W. F. HORN
RICHARD BOSCH AND SHELBY BOGGS.

THANKS TO ALL!

Machine Age To Jet Age

Radiomania's™ Guide to Tabletop Radios 1933-1959

TABLE OF CONTENTS

Machine Age To Jet Age

Radiomania's™ Guide to Tabletop Radios 1933-1959

TABLE OF CONTENTS

Machine Age To Jet Age

Radiomania's™ Guide to Tabletop Radios 1933-1959

TABLE OF CONTENTS

INTRODUCTION

Welcome to the first volume of Radiomania's vintage radio reference guides. In compiling this reference, it quickly became evident that, in order to do the subject justice, focus should be placed on specific areas of interest. Radio collectors seem to naturally find their niche in one particular area of collecting or another. Whether it be cathedrals, bakelites, catalins, tombstones, consoles, early battery sets, 1950s kitsch, machine age design, etc.

A common ground for many collectors is the tabletop radios of the high style era beginning in the early 1930s and continuing through the 1950s. It was during this period that industrial designers saw their heyday and radios became more than functional pieces of electronic equipment. They were icons of a new age in communication, designed to be consumed. Where radios are known to be attributed to major industrial designers we have so noted the designer in the description.

Since a picture is worth a thousand words, not much in the way of a written description is necessary. However, we have noted the materials used in constructing the radio, year of manufacture, coloration and average market value. Additionally, given the plethora of references available, it was decided to focus on the most desireable radios and those that are not pictured in other reference books. It is hoped that this will be a well received supplement to the collector's library.

PRICING

In compiling this book the question as to whether to include prices at all was one of major concern to both the author and contributors. As most collectors are aware, even the best price guide, if not initially flawed, is soon obsolete. The range of prices paid for most items is wide. One can pay anywhere from a few dollars to a few hundred for a given item, dependent on where it was purchased and from whom. Thus the task of establishing a 'market value' is difficult if not impossible. This problem given, it was still generally felt that the value of including prices, at least as a general market gauge, would outweigh the disadvantages of omitting them completely.

In establishing values a number of sources were utilized including auction results, classified ads, meet pricing, collector valuations and the author's personal experience having been both a collector and dealer for over ten years. Prices in this book represent items in average condition. Average meaning that the radio is intact but 'as found'. No repairs would have been made, either electrically or otherwise. If wood, the finish would be original. It might show some wear, but would be presentable in a collection once cleaned up. If plastic, the cabinet would be free from cracks and chips. Plaskon radios in average condition might evidence some minor stress lines but nothing which would detract from their aesthetics. Values followed by a '+' symbol represent rarer items, only a few of which have traded hands. In such cases the value listed represents an estimate of what a collector might expect to pay for an average example. The '+' symbol is also used to indicate baseline values for catalin radios, the price of which will vary widely based on color, condition, marbelization, and variations. This reference does not attempt to address the intricacies of valuing catalin radios, but merely to provide the reader with a baseline gauge.

A word about dealers and dealer prices: expect to pay a premium when purchasing from a dealer. The dealer offers one the luxury of eliminating the time consuming hunt through yard and estate sales, flea markets, antique shows and the like. It is he who goes through the trouble of rooting out those hard to find items. Ones which you might not happen upon except after years of hunting yourself. Dealers inventories represent long hours and related expenses and must reflect those additional costs.

FINE TUNING VALUES

To assist the collector in fine tuning the value of a given radio, some general rules of thumb are offered. Please remember that, as with all rules, there are exceptions to these. If you are unsure about a specific item you will always do best to ask another collector whom you trust.

GENERAL CONSIDERATIONS

CHASSIS CORROSION: In buying any radio it is important to visually inspect the chassis, particularly if you plan to restore the set to working order. Minor surface corrosion is typical and acceptable to all but the most finicky of collectors and should not deter from the value. Extreme corrosion can be an indication that the radio was submerged at one time or at least has seen a lot of humidity. If so, the bulk of the internal components may need to be replaced. Even if you plan only to display the radio, if it is so damaged its value will be decreased by the fact that it would be less desirable to most other collectors.

RODENT WEAR: Most of us have, at some time, come across a radio with leaves stuffed into the nooks and crannies of its chassis and acorns which have mysteriously gotten underneath, or a set which has had every wire, both exposed and internal, chewed through. Such phenomena are caused by common vermin such as squirrels, rats and mice. At one time the radio was probably stored outside in a barn or garage and it happened to become someones home. The damage caused by such occupancy can be severe. If you come across such a set and are tempted to buy it, inspect it carefully. The easily observed superficial problems may be but a sign of more extreme damage internally. Yank the chassis if you plan to restore it to working order. You may chose not to after you see the innards.

TRANSFORMERS: A common problem, and one that may be costly to remedy, is that of the 'smoked' transformer. Caused by a short circuit or overload, damage to the transformer almost always necessitates its replacement. Fortunately, such problems are often easy to spot. Look for smoke damage to the chassis and on the inside of the cabinet. Also look for gooey stuff (which may have hardened over time) oozing from the transformer itself. Most collectors stay far away from sets with blown transformers if at all possible. Short of finding a junker radio of the same variety but with a good transformer, you'll need to buy a replacement with the same specs.   This can cost anywhere from twenty to ninety dollars assuming you are lucky enough to even find a match.

TUBES: Missing tubes are generally easy to replace, particularly amongst radios from this era. The resources are numerous. Your local club will probably be your least expensive resource (usually one to three dollars per tube). After that there are local repair shops, mail order companies and specialty houses. It is a good idea to know your resources when considering the purchase of a radio sans tubes. Also be aware that there are critters known as ballast tubes which look like filament tubes superficially but which are really resistors. Count on about one out of every two ballast tubes needing replacement. Unlike filament tubes, few ballasts have survived.   Replacing a bad ballast will require much perseverance or some clever electronic rigging to bypass the device.

BACKS: Most radios pictured in this book had backs when they were originally sold. Most don't now. The backs were typically flimsy cardboard which became worn and fell off never to be seen again. Often times the antenna was attached to the missing back and is now also missing. To most collectors the absence of a cardboard back will not detract from the value of a radio. Conversely, the presence of a back, particularly if it is in good condition, will add value. One exception to this rule are those radios made during the mid to late 1930s with moulded plastic backs (like the Fada 260 series or the Emerson 199). With these radios the back is considered to be a critical element of the radio design and, as such, its absence can devalue a set by as much as 25%.

KNOBS: If one or more knobs are missing from a radio its value will be diminished. The purchaser of such a radio must resolve himself to either completing the set or substituting another complete set that looks right. If you chose to complete the set with correct knobs, the most cost effective, but also the most time consuming, method is to bring a correct knob with you to a local collector meet in hopes of finding a match in a box of odd knobs for sale. Cost for such knobs is typically in the one to five dollar range. Be prepared to wait a long time and look through a lot of boxes though. Another way to complete the set is to purchase a reproduction from one of several vendors throughout the country. Check ads in trade periodicals and club newsletters for such resources. There are dozens of types being reproduced and stocked today. The price for such reproduction knobs will range from two to seven dollars. Specialty knobs with chrome rings or those that duplicate catalin can run upwards of twenty-five dollars each. If you've got an odd bird which is not being reproduced, your final alternative is a specialty vendor who will make a casting of your knob with reproductions upon order. Cost for such knobs typically begins at ten dollars. Regardless of how you decide to deal with the missing knob(s), the value of the radio will be reduced by an amount which correlates directly with the time, cost and aggravation of completing the set.

DIAL LENSES: Covering the dial area on most radios pictured in this book is a plastic or glass dial lense. A damaged or missing plastic dial lense can be reproduced to order by a number of vendors. The going rate is about fifteen dollars per lense. If you don't have the original you can still make a tracing of the dial opening and send it to with your order. Again, look in periodicals and club bulletins for resources.

Glass dial lenses are typically made from convex round pieces of glass secured either inside the dial bezel or attached to the dial scale on the radio itself. Clockmakers usually will have matches for such pieces in the form of clock crystals. Just measure the outside diameter of the glass and make a few calls to area clockmakers or contact a supply house. You might, as an alternative, decide to replace the glass with plastic and contact a lense reproducer.

Both glass and plastic dial lenses were sometimes reverse painted with dial scales and ornamentation. If such a dial is broken, cracked, warped or otherwise damaged you've got a significant problem facing you. Except for a limited number of high value radios, no one makes reproduction dial scales. It will be next to impossible to find a suitable replacement. Your best hope will be to find another of the same radio and use its glass. You'd probbly do just as well to wait for that next radio instead. The only reasons to buy a radio with such a problem are either that the price is extremely reasonable (enough to make the problem tolerable) or that you do not expect to have another opportunity to own such a radio in the forseeable future.

PLASTICS

For the novice colllector the number of different plastics used in the manufacture of radio cabinets can be confusing. Furthermore, the names we use today have been established more from convention than anything else. That is, most all of the descriptive names currently used were at one time a brand or product name for the material. Typically, many manufacturers produced the same or a similar material. For one reason or another a single brand name has, over time, become synonymous with the material itself. The most common types of plastics and their conventions are as follows:

BAKELITE: The 'first' plastic, Bakelite was made from a powder and molded under tremendous pressure and heat. It is typically brown or black and somewhat pourous. Brown bakelite can be heavily 'mottled' with various shades of coloration.

BEETLE: Formed, like bakelite, under heat and pressure, this early plastic can be striking in appearance. Used to mold cabinets from the late 1930s through the early 1940s, beetle is typically opaque ivory in color with marbled streaks of orange, rust, geen, blue, red and brown. Some examples may be subtle with just a hint of rust marbelizing while others evidence themselves in a wide array of deep color tones.

CATALIN: An early resin, catalin was poured into molds and then cured in low heat ovens over a period of days. Once removed from the mold, if not broken in the process, the catalin radio cabinet was machined to remove debris and to add detail to the design. The labor intensity of this material was not at issue in the late 1930s when it was first introduced in radio cabinetry, but after World War II, with the shortage of manpower that resulted, its use quickly became cost prohibitive.

Catalin is known to be the most valuable of plastics used in radios with colorations ranging from opaque solid colors to semi-transluscent marbles resembling polished agate. Catalin is more fragile than other plastics of the period and is prone to chips, cracks, burns (from tube heat), discoloration (those butterscotch radios were originally white) and shrinking. All of these hazards have had a significant impact on the number of catalin sets which have survived, thus driving up their price.

PLASKON: Also manufactured using a process similar to bakelite, plaskon was molded in ivory and opaque colors. Typically, radio manufacturers offered the consumer the option of an ivory color at a higher price. Sometimes this was simply a painted brown or black bakelite cabinet. Other times it was molded in ivory plaskon. Occaisionally, radios were offered in colors other than ivory. Plaskon cabinets were available in colors such as pistaschio green, chinese red and lavender. Although plaskon wears about as well as bakelite, it is subject to stress lines. These are superficial cracks which, unfortunately, fill with dirt and grime over the years. Some can be cleaned or bleached out, others can be sanded down, but most must be lived with.

PLASTIC: Refers to contemporary injection molded plastics, most frequently polystyrene. First widely used in the late 1940s and available in a variety of colors.

TENITE: Occaisionally used for cabinets, tenite was most often used for the manufacture of radio grilles, knobs, handles and ornamental parts. The most significant problem with this material was its vulnerability to warpage due to proximity to heat. Tenite was not a particularly wise choice for use in construction of heated filament tube-type radios. Almost all tenite warps to one degree or another. The best one can hope for is minimal warpage.

VALUING PLASTIC RADIOS

CHIPS AND CRACKS: As a rule of thunb, a major flaw in any plastic radio, such as a significant visible chip, crack or warp, will cut the value of that radio in half so long as it remains displayable. Among plaskon radios hairline stress cracks are fairly common. In many models they are the rule and not the exception. As stated previously, so long as the stress lines are not too numerous and do not detract materially from the general aesthetics of the radio, the depreciation should be minimal. On the other hand, the stress free example of a set which is commonly found with stress lines is worth considerably more than average.

FRAGILITY: Dependent on the thickness of the casting, materials used in construction and the extremity of design, some radios are inherently more delicate than others. The most fragile (such as the Kadette 'Classic') are rarely found in near perfect condition. This 'universe' from which each radio is drawn must be considered in determining its value. In our example, a Kadette 'Classic' in what would appear to the casual observer as marginal condition, might, in fact, be an excellent example of that model, given the condition of other surviving sets.

REPAIRS: Although there have been some relatively successful attempts at bakelite repair, no repair can go undetected. A well repaired flaw can increase the value of a radio but will never raise its value to that of an unflawed one.

PAINT CHIPS: While many of these early plastic radios were available in different colors (typically walnut, black and ivory), oftentimes the ivory colored sets were brown or black bakelite which had been painted at the factory. This factory painting process was similar to that used in the automobile industry. After several layers of paint were applied, the cabinet was baked for several hours. As a result, the paint became 'hard' and much more susceptible to chipping over time. In addition to the problem of chipping, the baking process made the paint that much more difficult to remove. Stripping old baked on paint is extremely difficult and time intensive at best. Be prepared to use caustic chemicals and spend a lot of time. You may then find yourself with a black or brown radio and cast ivory plaskon knobs. This may look fine to you, but it is not 'original' and will be less valuable to other collectors. The net result is that the value of a factory painted radio with paint chips will be reduced by anywhere from ten to fifty percent dependent on the extent and placement of chipping.

VALUING WOOD RADIOS

Although typically not as popular with collectors in the past, wood cabinet radios are gaining in value and popularity as the hobby expands. It is interesting to note that, when radios were sold in the 1930s and 1940s, it was the wood cabinet which sold for a premium. Plastics were considered then to be a cheap man-made alternative.

The following are some basics to keep in mind when considering the purchase of a wood cabinet radio:

FINISH: Most wood radios produced during the 1930s through the 1950s were finished with either clear or toned lacquer. The more expensive sets were hand rubbed resulting in the 'piano' finish many today find so desireable. Over the years many things can and usually do happen to a lacquer finish. The finish will dry and chip, peel or separate ('alligator'). Rarely does one come across an original lacquer finish without some evidence of the passage of time. Unless the surviving finish is horrendous, it is worthwhile trying to salvage. There are various products available which will allow you to easily clean the surface and replenish the moisture in the lacquer. Additionally, you may want to amalgamize the finish to cover bare spots. This involves dissolving the original finish with denatured alcohol or other substance and respreading it.

As opposed to clear lacquer, toned lacquers present more of a problem. Many manufacturers, instead of using different wood veneers for contrast, used a single veneer type and sprayed toned lacquers for variations in color and shade. Originally, the difference was difficult to discern. Today it is evident. When toned lacquers age they reveal the original color of the wood underneath, usually in deep contrast. The darker the toner, the more significant the problem. The purchaser of such a radio must resign himself to live with the radio as is or refinish it. Both are a compromise.

VENEERS: Most all early radio cabinets were made with wood veneers as opposed to solid exotic or hardwoods. Over time the glue which bonds the veneer to the wood of the cabinet can deteriorate. The result ranges from small veneer chips to full pieces of veneer falling off. The best case is where the veneer is separating, but still present. This is easy to remedy with glue and clamps. If pieces of veneer are actually missing, they must obviously be replaced. This means removing the remainder of the damaged section of veneer and replacing it with another full piece. You may be able to find such a piece with an original finish on a junker radio. Otherwise, you will need to apply a finish to the new veneer. If the piece is very small and in a relatively concealed area you may chose to fill the hole with a matching wood puttly, shellac stick or toner pencil.

Additionally, veneer tends to lose its flexibility over time. Veneer which has been bent at angles of ninety degrees or more on a radio may break at those turns. If this occurs, again, be prepared to live with it or replace that entire section of veneer.

PAPER VENEER: A concept similar to the toned lacquer, paper veneer involved application of exotic veneer decals to the radio cabinet. This technique was used for both whole radio cabinets and small details. Upon close inspection of the veneer, one can usually discriminate between paper and real veneers. A damaged decal will make the difference apparent. If a radio is ornamented with damaged paper finish, any attempt to repair or refinish the radio will likely remove the decal or damage it further. This should be kept in mind when evaluating such a set for purchase.

REFINISHING: All but the absolute purists will agree that some radios just need to be refinished in order to be displayable. Many collectors have not seen a well refinished radio and so cannot appreciate the art to it. The process is long and involved, and extremely time intensive, but the result of a 'professional' refinish is astonishing. Of course there is refinishing and there is refinishing. Many collectors will use a caustic solvent to remove the original finish, then stain the cabinet and apply a coat of polyurethane or tung oil. The result is something that looks like it came out of a craft shop, not a vintage radio. If you are considering the purchase of a radio which is so refinished it should be valued as if it had no finish at all (about half the value of such a set in average condition).

Other types of refinishing are less objectionable and easier to remedy. Oftentimes one encounters a radio with the original finish intact. It is just underneath a coat of slopped on varnish or shellac. Various solvents can be used to remove the top coat and leave the original finish. There is an art to this process in both identifying the right solvent and its application. Read up on refinishing and talk to other collectors about their experiences before attempting this on a valuable acquisition. The net result on the value of radios so 'refinished' is a reduction by about twenty-five percent. A note of caution: be certain that the slopped on coat is not polyurethane. If it is, you're back to square one and must remove all finishes.

RESOURCES

As the hobby of vintage radio collecting has evolved over time, so have the resources for collectors. There are regional, national and international clubs. Cottage industries have sprung up offering a wide range of products and services. There are club newsletters, bulletins, references books and a monthly periodical on the subject. The following pages serve to provide the novice with some basic resources. This is, by far, not a comprehensive listing of all resources available. Any ommissions are not purposeful and do not reflect in any way on the individuals or organizations omitted.

VINTAGE RADIO CLUBS:

By far the best part of the hobby is meeting and spending time with other collectors. Club meets provide a forum for exchange of information, purchase of material and new radio acquisitions among other things. There are few collectors in the United States who are not within a few hours drive from a local or regional club. The following is a listing of regional, national and international clubs. When writing any organization for information be sure to include a postage paid return envelope to assure a response.

REGIONAL CLUBS (UNITED STATES)

Alabama Historical Radio Society
2413 Briar Trail, Birmingham, AL 35226

Antique Radio Collectors of Ohio
PO Box 292292, Kettering, OH 45429

Antique Radio Club of Illinois
RR3, 200 Langham, Morton, IL 61550

Arkansas Antique Radio Club (ARCA)
PO Box 191117, Little Rock, AR 72219

Antique Radio Club of Schenectady
915 Sherman St., Schenectady, NY 12303

Arizona Antique Radio Club
8311 E.Via de Sereno, Scottsdale, AZ 85258

Antique Radio Club of Ft. Smith
7917 Hermitage Dr., Ft. Smith, AR 72903

Belleville Area Antique Radio Club
219 W. Spring, Marissa, IL 62257

Antique Radio of Greater St. Louis
2015 Hickory Ridge Rd., Unoin, MO 63084

Buckeye Antique Radio Club
4572 Mark Trail, Copley, OH 44321

California Historical Radio Society (CHRS)
PO Box 31659, San Francisco, CA 94131

Houston Vintage Radio Association
PO Box 31276, Houston, TX 77231

CHRS-North Valley Chapter
15853 Ontario Pl., Redding, CA 96001

Hudson Valley Antique Radio & Phono
PO Box 1, Rt 207, Campbell Hall, NY 10916

Carolina Antique Radio Society
824 Fairwood Rd., Columbia, SC 29209

Hudson Valley Vintage Radio Club
507 Violet Ave., Hyde Park, NY 12538

Central NY/Northern PA Antique Radio Club
711 Elm St., Groton, NY 13073

Iowa Antique Radio Club & Historical Society
2191 Graham Cir., Dubuque, IA 52002

Cincinnati Antique Radio Collectors
6805 Palmetto, Cincinnati, OH 45227

Kentucky Chapter (ARCA)
3114 Boxhill Ct., Louisville, KY 40222

Colorado Radio Collectors
5270 E. Nassau Circle, Englewood, CO 80110

Indiana Historical Radio Society
725 College Way, Carmel, IN 46032

Connecticut Area Antique Radio Collectors
500 Tobacco St., Lebanon, CT 06249

Louisana & Mississippi Gulf Coast Area
1503 Admiral Nelson Dr., Slidell, LA 70461

Delaware Valley Historic Radio Club
PO Box 624, Lansdale, PA 19446

Michigan Antique Radio Club
PO Box 585, Okemos, MI 48864

Florida Antique Wireless Group
Box 738, Chuluota, FL 32766

Mid-America Antique Radio Club
220 Bayview, Lee's Summit, MO 64064

Greater Boston Antique Radio Collectors
12 Shawmut Ave., Cochituate, MA 01778

Mid-Atlantic Antique Radio Club
1312 Deep Run Lane, Reston, VA 22090

Greater NY Vintage Wireless Association
12 Garrity Ave., Ronkonkoma, NY 11779

Mid-South Antique Radio Collectors
811 Maple St., Providence, KY 42450

Hawaii Chapter (ARCA)
95-2044 Waikalani Pl., C-401, Mililani, HI 96789

Mississippi Historical Radio & Broadcasting
2412 C St., Meridian, MS 39301

Hawaii Historical Radio Club
45 Ala Kimo Dr., Honolulu, HI 96817

Mountains 'N' Plains Radio Collectors
1249 Solstice ln., Fort Collins, CO 80525

Music City Vintage Radio & Phono Society
PO Box 22291, Nashville, TN 37202

Society of Wireless Pioneers
146 Coleen St., Livermore, CA 94550

New England Antique Radio Club
17 Livingston Rd., Pelham, NH 03076

Southeastern Antique Radio Society
PO Box 500025, Atlanta, GA 31150

New Jersey Antique Radio Club
92 Joysan Terr., Freehold, NJ 07728

Southern California Antique Radio Society
6934 Orion Ave., VanNuys, CA 91406

Niagara Frontier Wireless Association
135 Autumnwood, Cheektowaga, NY 14227

Southern Vintage Wireless Association
3049 Box Canyon Rd., Huntsville, AL 35803

Northland Antique Radio Club
Box 18362, Minneapolis, MN 55418

South Florida Antique Radio Collectors
172 W. Flagler St., Ste .315, Miami, FL 33130

Northwest Vintage Radio Society
PO Box 82379, Portland, OR 97282

Tidewater Antique Radio Association
2328 Springfield, Ave., Norfolk, VA 23523

Oklahoma Vintage Radio
Collectors Club
PO Box 72-1197, Oklahoma City, OK 73172

Vintage Audio Listeners &
Valve Enthusiasts
1127 NW Bright Star Ln., Poulsbo, WA 98370

Pittsburgh Antique Radio Society, Inc.
407 Woodside Rd., Pittsburgh, PA 15221

Vintage Radio & Phonograph Society
PO Box 165345, Irving, TX 75016

Puget Sound Antique Radio Association
PO Box 125, Snohomish, WA 98291

Vintage Radio Unique Society
312 Auburndale St., Winston-Salem, NC 27104

Rhode Island Antique Radio
Enthusiasts
61 Columbus Ave., N. Providence, RI 02911

Western Wisconsin Antique Radio
Collectors
1611 Redfield St., La Crosse, WI 54601

Sacramento Historical Radio Society
PO Box 162162, Sacramento, CA 95816

West Virginia Chapter/ARCA
405 8th Ave., St. Albans, WV 25177

SPARK/Cincinnati Chapter
40 Dow Ct., Fairfield, OH 45014

Xtal Set Sociaty
789 N. 1500 Rd., Lawrence, KS 66049

SPARK/Columbus Chapter
2673 So. Dixie Dr., Dayton, OH 45409

U.S. NATIONAL AND INTERNATIONAL CLUBS:

Antique Wireless Association (AWA)*
Box E, Breesport, NY 14816

Antique Radio Club of America (ARCA)*
300 Washington Trails, Washington, PA 15301

International Antique Radio Club
PO Box 5261, Old Bridge, NJ 08857

E.H. Scott Historical Society
PO Box 1070, Niceville, FL 32588

Society for the Preservation of Antique Radio Knowledge (SPARKS)
2673 So. Dixie Dr., Dayton, OH 45409

* Note: AWA and ARCA are in the process of merging into one national club.

FOREIGN CLUBS:

AUSTRALIA

Historical Radio Society of Australia
PO Box 283, Mt. Waverly, Victoria 3149

CANADA

Canadian Vintage Radio Society
PO Box 43012, Metropolitan Pl. P.O.
Edmenton, Alberta T8A 5P9

London Vintage Radio Club
19 Honeysuckle Cres.
London, Ontario N5Y 4P3

Ottowa Vintage Radio Club
601-810 Edgeworth Ave.
Ottowa, Ontario K2B 5L5

ENGLAND

British Vintage Wireless Society
23 Rosendale Rd.
West Dulwich, London SE21 8DS

FRANCE

Club Histoire et Collection Radio
26 Rue de l'Oratoire, 54000 Nancy

French Antique Radio Association
135 Av. du President Wilson, 93100 Montreuil

GERMANY

German Society of Wireless History
Belm Tannenhof 55, 7900 Ulm 10

HOLLAND

N.V.H.R.
19, 6814 K.T., Ahmen

IRELAND

Irish Vintage Radio & Sound Society
39A Lower Drumconda Rd., Dublin 9

ISRAEL

Antique Radio & Broadcast Museum
24 Remez St., #7, Tel Aviv 62192

JAPAN

Antique Wireless Club
11-2-403 Hiroo, Shibuyaka, Tokyo 150

NEW ZEALAND

New Zealand Vintage Radio Society
20 Rimu Road, Mangere Bridge, Auckland

NORWAY

N.R.H.F.
PO Box 465 Sentrum, N-0105 Oslo 1

SPAIN

A.C.A.R.
55, 08840 Cardedeu, Barcelona

SWEDEN

Radio Historical Society
Gata 2, 417 55 Guteborg

The preceeding listing was provided courtesy of <u>Antique Radio Classified</u>
See Publications section for further information about this periodical.

PERIODICALS:

Antique Radio Classified is published monthly and is the foremost periodical dedicated to the hobby. Issues typically run in excess of 100 pages and include articles by collectors addressing technical issues, collecting, historic perspectives, test equipment, etc. Other regular features include a photo review of unusual items, meet and auction reports, club meeting notices, events calendars and, of course, a huge classified section. Additional information, including sample copies, can be obtained by writing Antique Radio Classified, P.O. Box 2-V79, Carlisle, MA 01741.

REFERENCE GUIDES:

Other books are available which provide a number of perspectives on the radio collecting hobby. These include the following:

Classic Plastic Radios of the 1930s and 1940s, Sideli
E.P. Dutton, 2 Park Avenue, NY, NY 10016

The Collector's Guide to Antique Radios, Volumes 1, 2 & 3, Bunis
Collector Books, PO Box 3009, Paducah, KY 42002-3009

Evolution of the Radio, Volumes 1 and 2
LW Books, PO Box 69, Gas City Indiana

A Flick of the Switch 1930-1950, McMahon
McMahon Vintage Radio, Box 1331, North Highlands, CA 95660

Golden Age of Radio in the Home and More Golden Age of Radio, Stokes
Craigs Printing co., Ltd., 67 Tay Street, Invercargill, New Zealand

Philco Radio 1928-1942, Ramirez & Prosise
Schiffer Publishing Ltd., 77 Lower Valley Road, Atglen, PA 19310

Radio Art, Hawes
Green Wood Publishing Co., Ltd., 6/7 Warren Mews, London W1P 5DJ

Zenith Radio Brochure Book, Jesperson & Emery
Great Northern, PO Box 17338, Minneapolis, MN 55417

OTHER RESOURCES: There are a host of suppliers and vendors who will make your life as a collector a little easier. Listed below are a representative few:

Antique Electronic Supply, 6221 S. Maple Avenue, Tempe, AZ 85283
Wholesale supplier of vintage tubes, electronic components, reproduction knobs, grille cloth and other items.

Constantine's, 2050 Eastchester Rd., Bronx, NY 10461 (718) 792-1600
Complete line of woodworking tools and supplies including veneers.

Golden Age Radio, 1609 Ceddox Lane, Baltimore, MD 21226
Professional Radio Repair. (410) 354-6533

Great Northern, PO Box 17338, Minneapolis, MN 55417
Wide range of NOS and reproduction Zenith parts and other items. Write for catalog.

Greenbaum Radio Refinishing, 312 S. Exeter St., Baltimore, MD 21202
Complete range of professional wood cabinet refinishing. (410) 752-2438

Michael Katz, 3987 Daleview Ave., Seaford, NY 11783
Reproduction radio grille cloth. Send $.52 LSASE for samples.

Kotton Kleanser Products, Inc., PO Box 1386, Braden, TN 38010-1386
Manufacturer of wood cleaner, protective wood feeder and other antique resoration products.

Vintage Radio & TV Supply, 3498 West 105th Street, Cleveland, OH 44111
Reproduction knobs, parts, tubes and other items. (216) 671-6712

Wades World of Knobs, 7109 E. Arbor Ave., Mesa, AZ 85208
Reproduction knobs and castings made to order. Write for catalog and information.

CA1934
WOOD
BRASS
ESCUTCHEONS

$90

5A
CA1947
WOOD

$325

2
CA1947
BEETLE &
PLASKON

$700+

5D
CA1947
CATALIN

$1000+

2A
CA1947
CATALIN

$850+

7
CA1946
WOOD

$50

Addison

51
CA1948
WOOD

$75

55
CA1950
BAKELITE

$60

L2F
CA1946
CATALIN

$750+

CA1935
WOOD
2-TONE
LACQUER

$110

CA1939
BAKELITE

$110

CA1936
WOOD
'SKYSCRAPER'

$250

5-J3
CA1952
PLASTIC
CLOCK-
RADIO

$35

CA1938
PLASKON

$90

5-Z23
CA1949
BAKELITE

$35

16-D25
CA1941
BAKELITE

$110

361-5Q
CA1938
PLASKON

$125

113-A5
CA1937
BAKELITE

$125

396-6M
CA1940
BAKELITE

$125

162
CA1938
BAKELITE

$65

551
CA1936
WOOD

$145

577-5Q
CA1939
BAKELITE

$110

'JUNIOR'
CA1939

BAKELITE
$75

RED
PLASKON
$250+

990-6Y
CA1938
3-POSITION
BAKELITE
CHROMIUM
TRIM

$175

P5035
CA1947
WOOD
'LYRE' GRILLE

$50

B325
CA1937
WOOD

$75

'PEE WEE'
CA1946
BAKELITE

$60

'SKY KING'
CA1935
WOOD W/
DECO CUT-OUTS

$40

CA1937
WOOD
MIDGET

$60

CA1935
WOOD W/
DECO CUT-OUTS

$45

120
CA1934
WOOD
W/CRYSTALLINE
NAPHTHALINE
FINISH

$750+

CA1935
WOOD W/
DECO CUT-OUTS

$60

52
CA1933
BAKELITE

$2000+

52
CA1933
'EGYPTIAN'
BAKELITE

$2000+

A600
'DUCHESS'
CA1947
BLACK BAKELITE
& WHITE
PLASKON,
CATALIN KNOBS

$300

A400
CA1947
BAKELITE

$50

A600
'DUCHESS'
CA1947
CATALIN

$600+

A520
CA1948
PLASTIC

$45

CA1937
BAKELITE
W/RED
HIGHLIGHTS

$80

CA1947
(BELMONT)
BAKELITE

$75

CA1938
MIDGET
BAKELITE

$85

O4BR-
5O8A
CA 1939
(BELMONT)
BAKELITE

$125

CA1940
BAKELITE

$60

O4BR-
514B
CA 1939
(BELMONT)
BAKELITE

$95

05GCB-
1541
CA 1951
(MAJESTIC)
BAKELITE

$800+

54BR-
150JR
CA 1937
(BELMONT)
BAKELITE

$90

14BR-
1501B
CA 1941
(BELMONT)
BAKELITE

$60

62-140
CA1937
(BELMONT)
WOOD
W/BAKELITE
ESCUTCHEON

$90

14BR-
750L
CA 1940
(BELMONT)
WOOD

$85

62-148
CA1937
(BELMONT)
WOOD
W/BAKELITE
ESCUTCHEON

$90

62-151
CA1935
WOOD

$110

62-245
CA1937
(BELMONT)
WOOD
W/BAKELITE
ESCUTCHEON

$90

62-196
CA1935
WOOD

$95

62-288
'MIRACLE'
CA1938
BAKELITE

$100

62-198
CA1937
(BELMONT)
WOOD
W/BAKELITE
ESCUTCHEON

$85

62-316
CA1936
WOOD

$70

62-325
CA1937
(WELLS
GARDNER)
BAKELITE

$100

62-386
CA1937
(WELLS
GARDNER)
BAKELITE

$115

62-352
CA1937
(WELLS
GARDNER)
BAKELITE

$125

62-445
CA1937
(WELLS
GARDNER)
BAKELITE

$135

62-355
CA1937
(WELLS
GARDNER)
BAKELITE

$135

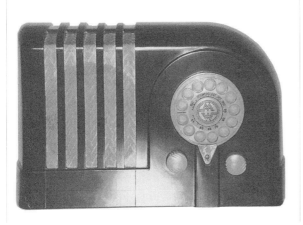

62-453
CA1938
BAKELITE

$110

62-505
CA1938
(WELLS GARDNER)
BAKELITE

$110

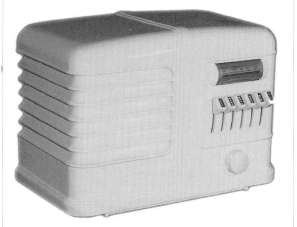

93-WG-
542A
CA1939
(WELLS
GARDNER)
BAKELITE

$150

84BR-
1407
CA1939
(BELMONT)
BAKELITE

$95

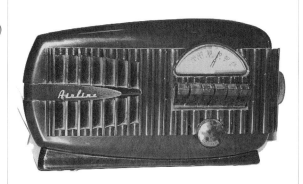

93-WG-
601
CA1939
(WELLS
GARDNER)
BAKELITE

$150

84KR-
1520
CA1949
(ARVIN)
MIDGET METAL

$65

306
CA 1937
WOOD

$75

40
'Mighty Mite'
CA1938
Metal
Midget

$110

302A
CA1938
Metal
Radio-Phono
Chrome Trim

$150

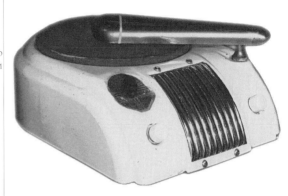

58
CA1940
Bakelite

$80

341T
CA1950
Metal
Midget

$65

243T
CA1948
Metal
Midget

$60-90
Dependent on
Color

402
CA1939
Metal
Midget

$75

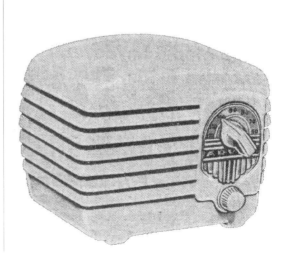

417
'RHYTHM
BABY'
CA1938
WOOD
MINI-
TOMBSTONE

$225

444
CA1946
METAL
MIDGET

$65

44OT
CA1950
METAL
MIDGET

$60-85
DEPENDENT ON
COLOR

467
'RHYTHM
BELLE'
CA1936
WOOD

$85

441T
'HOPPY'
CA1950
METAL
MIDGET
FOIL FRONT OF
HOPALONG
CASSIDY

$350
(WARNING:
FOIL FRONTS
BEING REPRO-
DUCED)

5O2
CA1940
METAL
MIDGET

$85

508
(PHANTOM
SERIES)
CA1936
WOOD

$75

522A
CA1940
METAL
MIDGET

$75

517
'RHYTHM
JUNIOR'
CA1938
WOOD

$200

532A
CA1941
CATALIN

$1200+

518
'PHANTOM
BABY'
CA1936
WOOD
SQUAT TOMBSTONE

$125

540T
CA1951
METAL
MIDGET

$60-80
DEPENDENT ON
COLOR

544AR
CA1946
BAKELITE

$70

617
'RHYTHM
MAID'
CA1938
WOOD

$225

568A
'PHANTOM
BLONDE'
CA1936
WOOD

$145

618
'PHANTOM
JUNIOR'
CA1936
WOOD

$90

602A
CA1940
BAKELITE

$85

632
CA1941
WOOD

$45

702
CA1940
WOOD

$110

2581
CA1958
OLIVE PLASTIC

$50

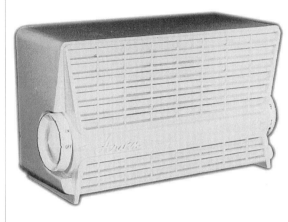

732
CA1941
WOOD

$45

R281-1
CA1950
BAKELITE
W/LUCITE
COVERED DIAL
BEZEL

$50

840T
CA1954
METAL
MIDGET

$60-85
DEPENDENT ON
COLOR

RE267
CA1955
MARBLED
PLASTIC

$55

155
CA1933
WOOD
W/MARQUETRY

$150

206
CA1934
WOOD

$325

167
CA1933
WOOD

$225

217
CA1933
WOOD

$275

185B
CA1935
WOOD
METAL INLAY

$250

255
CA1936
WOOD

$225

275
CA1933
WOOD

$200

555
'MUSIC
BOX'
CA1933
WOOD
MARQUETRY

$350

447
CA1933
WOOD
MARQUETRY

$350

708
CA1933
WOOD

$450

456
CA1936
WOOD

$175

725
CA1936
WOOD

$150

825

CA1934
WOOD
MARQUETRY

$175

854

CA1935
WOOD
W/MARQUETRY

$175

944

CA1934
WOOD
2-TONE
LACQUER

$225

5D114
CA1946
BAKELITE

$200

51O
CA1938
BAKELITE

$135

5D128
CA1946
BAKELITE

$175

519
CA1939
BAKELITE

$225

6D111
CA1946
BAKELITE

$135

526
CA1938
BAKELITE

$200

602
'SCOTTY'
CA1938
BAKELITE

$225

401
CA1938
WOOD
W/BAKELITE
ESCUTCHEON

$90

CA1938
BAKELITE

$200

65P4U
CA1949
BAKELITE
w/METAL
GRILLE

$40

75P6U
CA1949
BAKELITE
w/METAL
GRILLE

$50

55P2U
CA1949
BAKELITE

$40

111
CA1947
BAKELITE

$40

55P3U
CA1949
BAKELITE
w/METAL
GRILLE

$60

112
CA1947
WOOD

$40

Bendix

114
CA1947
SWIRLED PLASTIC

$300

526D
CA1946
BAKELITE

$60

301
CA1948
WOOD

$40

O526E
CA1946
WOOD
CURVED
GRILLE

$55

526C
CA1946
CATALIN

$625

626C
CA1947
BAKELITE

$45

636C
CA1946
WOOD
W/WOVEN
METAL GRILLE

$60

753M
CA1953
WOOD
CLOCK-RADIO

$40

953A
CA1953
PLASTIC

$30

Climax

CA1934
WOOD

$85

CA1936
WOOD
SMALL
TOMBSTONE
2-TONE
LACQUER

$125

CA1936
WOOD
MINI-
CONSOLE

$300

CA1937
WOOD

$95

CA1936
WOOD

$60

CA1938
WOOD

$125

CA1938
WOOD
DECO
CUTOUTS

$125

'EMERALD'
CA1937
WOOD

$425

'CRUSADER'
CA1935
WOOD
ALUMINUM
TRIM

$225

'OPAL'
CA1937
WOOD

$650

'DIAMOND'
CA1937
WOOD

$575

'RUBY'
CA1938
WOOD

$650

CA1933
WOOD
MARQUETRY

$125

301
CA1934
WOOD
CHROME GRILLE

$350+

2001
CA1933
WOOD
MARQUETRY
INSERT GRILLE

$175

654
CA1933
WOOD
MARQUETRY

$75

300
CA1935
BAKELITE
CHROMIUM
GRILLE & TRIM

$350

'NEW
WORLD'
CA1933
BAKELITE

BROWN $850

BLACK
$1000

IVORY
$1200

CA1935
WOOD

$65

CA1939
BAKELITE
(BELMONT)

$120

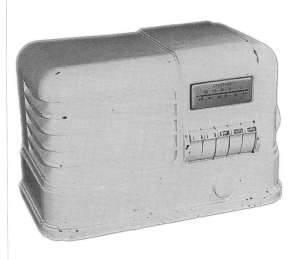

CA1935
WOOD

$65

110
CA1936
WOOD

$50

CA1936
WOOD

$90

43-8190
CA1947
PLASTIC
SWIRED PLASTIC
TRIM

$300

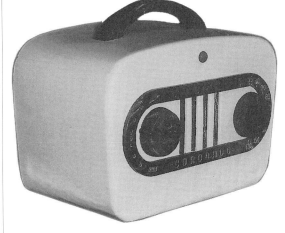

CA1934
WOOD
CHROME GRILLE
BLACK LACQUER
& CHROME TRIM

$300+

CA1946
WOOD

$45

'VANITY'
CA1942
BAKELITE

$85

'FIVER'
CA1934
WOOD
CHROME
ESCUTCHEON

$90

CA1939
BAKELITE

$80

'FIVER'
CA1934
WOOD
CHROME
ESCUTCHEON

$110

'FIVER'
CA1934
WOOD

$75

8
CA1934
WOOD
CHROME
ESCUTCHEON

$90

'FIVER'
CA1937
WOOD

$125

10-135
CA1953
BAKELITE

$85

5V2
CA1934
WOOD
CHROME
ESCUTCHEON

$90

10-AA
CA1939
BAKELITE

$80

CROSLEY

11-101U
CA1953
BAKELITE

$110

11-AB
CA1941
BAKELITE

$50

11-115U
CA1953
BAKELITE

$125

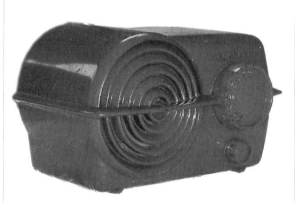

11-AC
CA1941
WOOD

$45

11-805U
CA1952
BAKELITE

$65

12-AB
CA1941
WOOD

$50

14-AG
CA1941
WOOD

$75

24-AU
CA1941
WOOD

$65

21-AQ
CA1941
WOOD

$45

25-AW
CA1941
WOOD

$75

24-AJ
CA1941
WOOD

$65

40
CA1934
WOOD
CHROME
ESCUTCHEONS

$95

41
CA1934
METAL
'LUNCHBOX'
TYPE

$110

56-PB
CA1946
BAKELITE

$45

41
'DELUXE'
CA1934
WOOD
CHROME
ESCUTCHEONS

$100

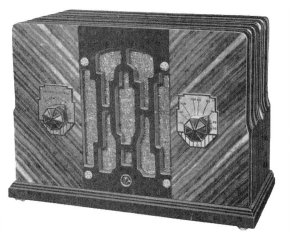

56-TD
'DUETTE'
CA1947

$125

52
CA1934
WOOD
CHROME
ESCUTCHEONS

$90

61-AF
CA1934
WOOD
CHROME BEZEL

$110

72-AF
CA1934
WOOD
CHROME BEZEL

$110

179
CA1934
WOOD
CHROME
ESCUTCHEONS

$125

80-AW
CA1934
WOOD
CHROME BEZEL

$125

181
CA1934
WOOD
CHROME
ESCUTCHEONS

$100

167
CA1933
WOOD
2-TONE
LACQUER

$165

179
CA1934
WOOD
CHROME
ESCUTCHEONS
SLIVER
FLUTING

$300

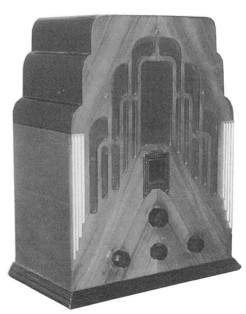

250
CA1937
WOOD
2-TONE
LACQUER

$110

299
CA1937
WOOD

$60

251
CA1937
WOOD

$80

349
CA1937
WOOD
TRAPEZOID

$95

295
CA1937
WOOD
DECO CUT-OUTS

$70

449
CA1937
WOOD

$90

495
CA1937
WOOD
DECO CUT-OUT

$120

605
CA1935
WOOD

$90

516
CA1936
WOOD

$80

689
CA1939
WOOD

$110

517
CA1940
COPPER
CABINET,
BAKELITE
GRILLE

$50

719
CA1941
BAKELITE

$75

B-548A
CA1939
BAKELITE

$75

D-25-E
CA1953
BAKELITE
CLOCK-RADIO

$90

C-516
CA1937
WOOD

$45

'DUAL
FIVER'
CA1934
WOOD
CHROME BEZEL

$125

C-529B
CA1939
BAKELITE

$75

E-15-CE
CA1953
BAKELITE

$75

F-5-TWE
'MUSICAL
CHEF'
CA1958
PLASTIC
RADIO/FOOD
TIMER

$75

G-1465
CA1938
CATALIN

$1500+

DELCO

CA1935
MIRROR

$750

1101
CA1934
WOOD

$80

CA1947
(BELMONT)
BAKELITE

$150

R1170
CA1947
BAKELITE

$55

CA1947
(BELMONT)
BAKELITE

$150

R1230
'RIBBON
GRILLE'
CA1946
BAKELITE

$60

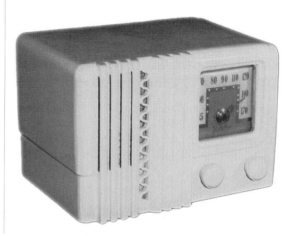

'PYRAMID'
CA1934
WOOD
2-TONE
LACQUER

$125

CA1935
WOOD

$125

CA1934
WOOD
BLACK LACQUER
DETAIL

$250

1731
CA1934
WOOD
CHROME GRILLE

$135

CA1935
WOOD

$225

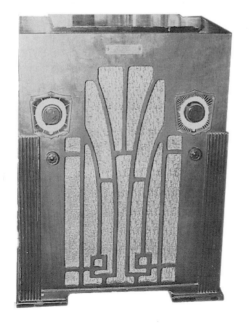

DETROLA

CA1934
WOOD
MARQUETRY

$75

CA1936
WOOD
MULTI-COLORED
MARQUETRY

$225

CA1935
WOOD

$120

'WOOD
BLUEBIRD'
CA1936
WOOD

$1000+

CA1936
WOOD

$125

47
CA1935
WOOD
'KIDNEY-SHAPE
CABINET'

$110

100
CA1936
WOOD

$135

117
CA1937
WOOD

$110

104
'EXECUTIVE'
CA1936
WOOD
LIMITED
PRODUCTION
PRESENTATION
DESK SET

$350

134
CA1939
WOOD
W/BEETLE BEZEL
& KNOBS

$125

109
CA1937
WOOD

$110

134A
CA1939
WOOD

$60

DETROLA

134B
CA1939
WOOD
W/BEETLE BEZEL
& KNOBS

$125

212
CA1939
WOOD

$50

199
'SUPER
PEEWEE'
CA1939
WOOD

$175

218
'PEEWEE'
CA1939

BAKELITE
$300

WHITE PLASKON
$400

OTHER COLORS
$750+

208
CA1939
BAKELITE

$70

219
'SUPER
PEEWEE'
CA1939

BAKELITE
$225

COLORED
PLASKON BODY
WITH BEETLE
GRILLE
$750+

280
'JUNIOR'
CA1939

BAKELITE
$150

COLORED
PLASKON
$350+

310
CA1940
WOOD
ORNATE
MARQUETRY

$120

281
'SPLIT GRILLE'
CA1939

CATALIN
$2000+

BEETLE PLASTIC
BODY
w/COLORED
PLASKON TRIM
$1000+

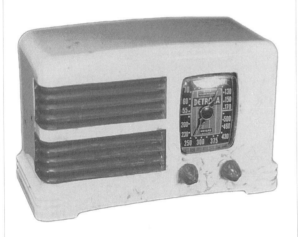

320
CA1940
WOOD
'SPLIT GRILLE'

$175

283
CA1939
BEETLE PLASTIC

$275+

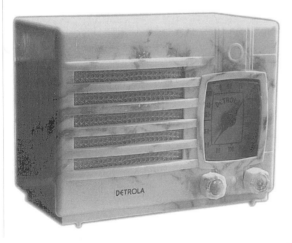

327
CA1940
BAKELITE
w/TENITE
GRILLE

$125

DETROLA

330
CA1940
WOOD

$150

532-1
CA1938
WOOD

$95

343
CA1940
'SPLIT GRILLE'
BAKELITE
W/TENITE
GRILLE INSERTS

$125

568-1
CA1947
METAL

GREY
HAMMERTONE
FINISH
$65

FACTORY
CHROMED
$100

440
'PEE WEE'
CA1939
WOOD

$300+

CA1936
WOOD

$75

406R
'BANTAM'
CA1938
BAKELITE
W/PLASKON FEET
& KNOBS

$250

CA1939
BAKELITE

$225

515
CA1936
WOOD

$85

CA1939
WHITE PLASKON
W/RED
PLASKON TRIM

$125

518
CA1937
WOOD

$50

DeWALD

54A

'DYNETTE'
CA1933
WOOD
INGRAHAM
CABINET

$110

615

CA1936
WOOD
INGRAHAM
CABINET

$200

550

'DYNETTE'
CA1933
WOOD
INGRAHAM
CABINET

$150

618

CA1937
WOOD

$80

580

'DELUXE'
CA1933
WOOD
INGRAHAM
CABINET

$225

619

CA1937
WOOD

$80

620
CA1937
WOOD

$75

'CROWN'
CA1934
WOOD

$95

901B
CA1937
WOOD

$150

JD519
CA1947
PLASKON

$55

A-501
'HARP'
CA1946
CATALIN

$500+

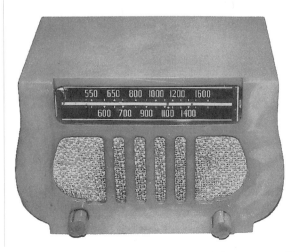

CA1934
WOOD
INGRAHAM
CABINET
SLIDE-TO-THE-
SIDE DOORS

$175

CA1939
WOOD
INGRAHAM
CABINET

$225

CA1938
BAKELITE
$80

WHITE PLASKON
$100

COLORED
PLASKON
$225+

CA1940
'PATRIOT'
SERIES
WOOD
INGRAHAM
CABINET
RED, WHITE &
BLUE STRIPING

$125

CA1939
WOOD
INGRAHAM
CABINET

$110

CA1940
WOOD
INGRAHAM
CABINET

$125

CA1940
WOOD
INGRAHAM
CABINET

$150

19
'MIRACLE
SIX'
CA1934
BAKELITE

$125

CA1940
WOOD
INGRAHAM
CABINET

$150

20A
CA1934
BAKELITE

$140

17
'MIRACLE
SIX'
CA1934
BLACK BAKELITE
W/CHROMIUM
TRIM

$350+

23
CA1935
WOOD
INGRAHAM
CABINET

$90

25
CA1933
WOOD
INGRAHAM
CABINET

$110

31
CA1934
WOOD
REPWOOD
FACE
BACKLIT DIALS

$225

28
CA1934
WOOD
INGRAHAM
CABINET

$135

31A
CA1934
WOOD
ALUMINUM
TRIM
BLACK METAL
GRILLE INSERT

$350+

30
CA1934
WOOD
INGRAHAM
CABINET
DROP-FRONT

$165

32
CA1934
WOOD
INGRAHAM
CABINET
BACKLIT DIALS

$140

34
CA1935
WOOD
INGRAHAM
CABINET

$100

45
CA1935
WOOD
INGRAHAM
CABINET

$125

38
CA1935
WOOD
INGRAHAM
CABINET

$150

49
CA1935
WOOD
INGRAHAM
CABINET

$450

42
CA1935
WOOD
INGRAHAM
CABINET

$375

106
CA1936
WOOD
INGRAHAM
CABINET

$200

107
CA1936
WOOD
INGRAHAM
CABINET

$175

111
CA1936
WOOD
INGRAHAM
CABINET

$175

108
'U5A'
CA1936
BAKELITE
MINI-
TOMBSTONE

BROWN $225
BLACK $250
WHITE $300

116
CA1936
WOOD
INGRAHAM
CABINET

$75

110
CA1936
WOOD
MINI-
TOMBSTONE
INGRAHAM
CABINET

$225

119
CA1936
WOOD
INGRAHAM
CABINET

$165

130
CA1937
WOOD
INGRAHAM
CABINET

$70

133
CA1937
WOOD
INLAID BRASS
INGRAHAM
CABINET

$225

131
CA1937
WOOD
INGRAHAM
CABINET

$65

134
CA1937
WOOD
OVERSIZED
TOMBSTONE
INGRAHAM
CABINET

$250

132
CA1937
WOOD
REPWOOD
FACE

$110

141
CA1937
WOOD
INGRAHAM
CABINET

$200

148
CA1937
WOOD
INGRAHAM
CABINET

$300

157
'CLOCKETTE'
CA1937
BAKELITE,
PLASKON

BROWN
$110
WHITE $135
BLACK & WHITE
$160

149
CA1937
BAKELITE

$70

159
CA1937
WOOD
INGRAHAM
CABINET

$225

153
CA1937
WOOD
INGRAHAM
CABINET

$120

167
CA1937
WOOD
INGRAHAM
CABINET

$125

169
CA1937
WOOD
RED INLAY
INGRAHAM
CABINET

$145

190
CA1938
CATALIN
MINI-
TOMBSTONE

$1200+

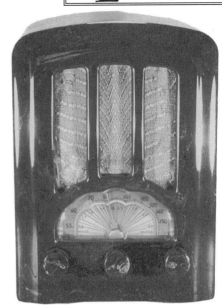

173
CA1937
WOOD
INGRAHAM
CABINET

$175

196
CA1938
WOOD
CONICAL DIAL
INGRAHAM
CABINET

$650

179
CA1937
WOOD
INGRAHAM
CABINET

$70

197
'MAE
WEST'
CA1938
WOOD
CONICAL DIAL
AND SPEAKER
INGRAHAM
CABINET

$1250+

198
'MYSTERY'
CA1938
BAKELITE

$90

201
CA1938
WOOD
INGRAHAM
CABINET

$90

199
CA1938
BAKELITE

$125

208
CA1938
BAKELITE

$85

200
CA1938
PLASKON

$110

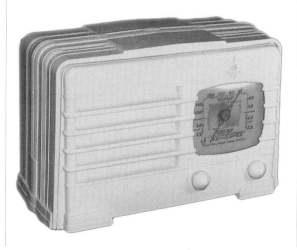

210
CA1938
WOOD
INLAID RED &
BLACK
INGRAHAM
CABINET

$135

211
'LITTLE MIRACLE'
CA1938

BROWN
BAKELITE
W/BLACK FEET
$95

WHITE PLASKON
W/BLACK FEET
$165

214
CA1938
WOOD
INGRAHAM
CABINET

$125

212
CA1938
WOOD
'BULLSEYE'
GRILLE
INGRAHAM
CABINET

WALNUT
W/INLAID
PISTACHIO
$225

MAPLE
W/INLAID
OXBLOOD
$375

217
CA1938
WOOD
INGRAHAM
CABINET

WALNUT $125

MAPLE $175

213
CA1938
WOOD
MINI-
TOMBSTONE
INGRAHAM
CABINET

$325

229
CA1938
WOOD
'HEXAGON'
CONICAL DIAL
INGRAHAM
CABINET

$425

231
CA1938
WOOD
CONICAL DIAL
INGRAHAM
CABINET

$200

245
CA1939
CATALIN
MINI-
TOMBSTONE

$1200+

235
'LITTLE
MIRACLE'
CA1938
CATALIN

$900+

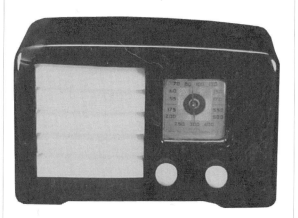

246
'D-DIAL'
CA1939

BROWN
BAKELITE
$140

IVORY PLASKON
$250

LIGHT GREEN
PLASKON
$350

238
'JEWEL BOX'
CA1939
INGRAHAM
CABINET

$325

247
'SNOW
WHITE'
CA1939
REPWOOD FACE
WOOD CABINET

$1700+

250
CA1933
WOOD
INGRAHAM
CABINET

$110

257
'KITCHENETTE'
CA1939
WOOD
INGRAHAM
CABINET

$250

255
'EMERSONETTE'
CA1939

BROWN
BAKELITE
$125

IVORY PLASKON
$150

GREEN OR RED
PLASKON
$350+

258
'BIG
MIRACLE'
CA1939
CATALIN

$600+

256
'STRAD'
CA1939
WOOD
INGRAHAM
CABINET

WALNUT
$500

MAPLE
$650

NOTE:
SUBTRACT $50-
100 FOR
SQUARE DIAL
OPENING

262
CA1939
WOOD
MIDGET
INGRAHAM
CABINET

$175

271
CA1939
WOOD
INGRAHAM
CABINET

$150

288
'BIG STRAD'
CA1939
WOOD
INGRAHAM
CABINET

$250

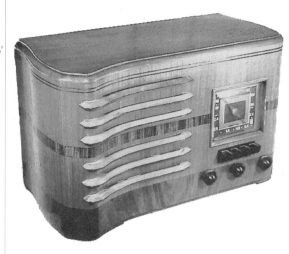

274
CA1939
BAKELITE

$110

295
CA1939
WOOD
INLAID RED
INGRAHAM
CABINET

$135

282
CA1939
WOOD
RED INLAY
INGRAHAM
CABINET

$185

300
CA1934
SMALL TREASURE
CHEST
WOOD
CHROME TRIM
INGRAHAM
CABINET

$150

313
CA1940
WOOD
INGRAHAM
CABINET

$110

317
CA1940
WOOD
CHROME INLAY
INGRAHAM
CABINET

$165

315
CA1940
WOOD
CONICAL
SPEAKER
INGRAHAM
CABINET

$125

320
CA1940
WOOD
W/BRASS
CORNER
GUARDS
INGRAHAM
CABINET

$150

316
CA1940
WOOD
INGRAHAM
CABINET

$225

334
CA1940
WOOD
INGRAHAM
CABINET

$65

336

CA1940

BAKELITE

(BELL GEDDES
ATTRIB.)

$110

399

CA1942

WOOD

INGRAHAM
CABINET

$110

350

CA1941

WOOD

INGRAHAM
CABINET

$165

400

'PATRIOT',
'ARISTOCRAT'

CA1942

(BEL GEDDES
DES.)

CATALIN

$500+

356

CA1941

WOOD

INGRAHAM
CABINET

$175

402

CA1942

WOOD

INGRAHAM
CABINET

$90

410
'MICKEY MOUSE'
CA1934
WOOD
CHROME TRIM

$1800

418
CA1942
WOOD
W/CONICAL
SPEAKER

$225

411
'MICKEY MOUSE'
CA1934
REPWOOD

$1800

WARNING:
REPWOOD
CABINETS BEING
REPRODUCED

436
CA1942
WOOD
INGRAHAM
CABINET

$75

414
'WHEAT'
CA1934
REPWOOD

$225

440
CA1942
WOOD
INLAID RED
INGRAHAM
CABINET

$185

504
CA1946
WOOD
W/LUCITE
FACEPLATE

$75

543
CA1947
BAKELITE

$45

517
'MODERNE'
CA1946
(LOEWY DES.)

BROWN, BLACK
OR WHITE
$70

SWIRLED BLACK
OR WHITE WITH
GOLD
$110

SWIRLED GREEN
OR RED WITH
GOLD
$150

544
CA1947
WOOD

$75

520
CA1946
CATALIN

$125+

547
CA1947
PLASTIC

$45

561
CA1948
(Loewy Des.)
Bakelite

$70

587A
CA1949
Plastic

$50

570
'Momento'
CA1949
Wood
Ingraham
Cabinet

$175

587
CA1949
Wood
Ingraham
Cabinet

$70

572
'Clockette'
CA1949
Plastic

$95

610
CA1949
(Loewy
Attr.)
Plastic

$75

Emerson

615B
CA1949
(LOEWY
ATTR.)
WOOD
INLAID OXBLOOD
INGRAHAM
CABINET

$125

744B
CA1954
PLASTIC

$300+

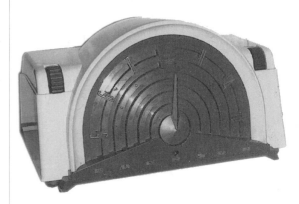

616A
CA1949
(LOEWY
ATTR.)
WOOD
INLAID
OXBLOOD
INGRAHAM
CABINET

$125

810
CA1955
PLASTIC

$35

724
CA1953
PLASTIC

$35

893
CA1958
WOOD
INGRAHAM
CABINET

$135

TYPE L
'BARONET'
CA1932
WOOD
TREASURE
CHEST

$250

U4B
CA1935
WOOD
INGRAHAM
CABINET

$110

TYPE L
'REGAL'
CA1932
WOOD

$85

TYPE L
AC5
CA1932
WOOD
TREASURE
CHEST

$300

CA1940
BAKELITE

$100

CA1947
PLASKON

$110

BROWN $90

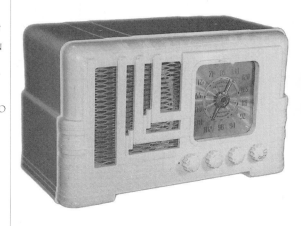

CA1947
BAKELITE

$95

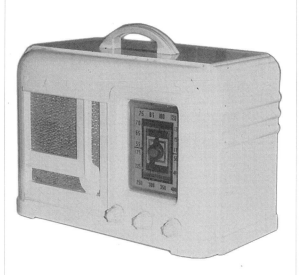

5F60
CA1937
CATALIN

$750+

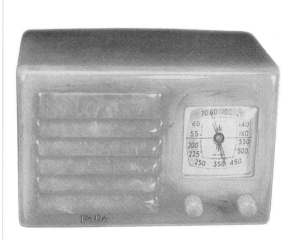

CA1947
BAKELITE

$90

52
CA1938
CATALIN

$1500+

115
'Bullet'
ca1940
Catalin

$500+

200
ca1951
Plastic
Clock-Radio

$60

119
ca1942
Plaskon

$110

Brown $90

246
ca1936
Bakelite,
Plaskon

Brown $150
Black & Chrome $300
Black & Gold $300
Ivory $225
Ivory & Gold $325
Red $325
Red & Gold $500+

167
ca1936
Wood

$125

250T
ca 1946
Wood

$140

252
'TEMPLE'
CA1941
CATALIN

$500+

260B
CA1936
BLACK
BAKELITE

$125

IVORY $150

RED $300

252
'TEMPLE'
CA1941
WOOD

$325

263W
CA1936
WOOD

$250

260G
CA1936
IVORY
PLASKON
w/GOLD
OVERLAY
TRIM

$250

BLACK &
CHROME
$300

RED & GOLD
$500

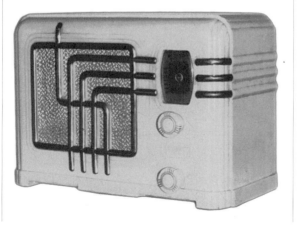

352J
CA1937
WOOD

$75

454B
CA1938
BAKELITE

BROWN
$100

BLACK $110

IVORY $140

740
CA1947
BAKELITE

$70

IVORY $100

454G
CA1938
IVORY
PLASKON
W/GOLD
TRIM

$250

BLACK &
CHROME

$300

790
CA1948
BAKELITE
$90

IVORY $110

550
CA1942
SWIRLED
PLASTIC

$85

830
CA1950
SWIRLED PLASTIC

$85

845
CA1950
SWIRLED
PLASTIC

$325+

A66
CA1939
WOOD
INGRAHAM
CABINET

$110

1005
CA1947
PLASTIC

$225+

B20
CA1936
'SILENT
RADIO'

SATINWOOD
VENEER
$300

CORK VENEER
$225

1216T
CA1937
WOOD

$1000+

F55
CA1938
WOOD
MIDGET

$150

L96W
CA1939
BAKELITE

$90

P80
CA1947
BAKELITE
CATALIN KNOB

$125

CA1948
BAKELITE
MARBLED
PLASTIC GRILLE

$45

AT23
CA1941
WOOD

$85

AT12
CA1939
BAKELITE

$90

CT43
CA 1942
BAKELITE

$45

AT14
CA1941
BAKELITE

$125

GTO51
'BULLET'
CA1948
BAKELITE

$110

27D
CA1938
WOOD

$80

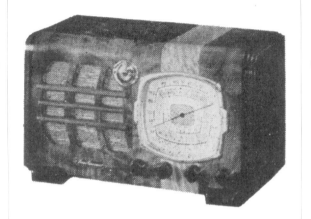

99
CA1938
WOOD

$70

28
CA1937
WOOD

$50

BG-357-P
CA1936
MIRRORED

$1200+

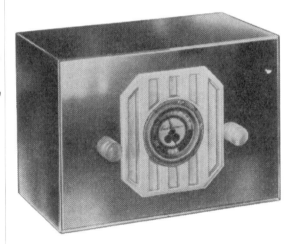

50
CA1937
WOOD

$90

FE-24
CA1937
WOOD

$50

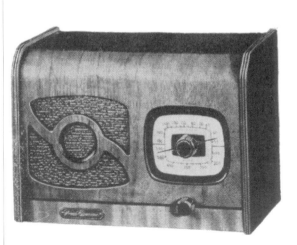

FE-65
CA1937
WOOD

$70

FE-68
CA1936
WOOD

$110

CA1933
WOOD
2-TONE
LACQUER

$110

2O2
CA1947
BAKELITE

$35

CA1933
WOOD
2-TONE
LACQUER

$150

4OO
CA1939
BAKELITE
'PEE WEE'

$125

CA1946
BAKELITE
W/CATALIN
TRIM

$125

44O
CA1954
BAKELITE
'ATOMIC' KNOB

$45

8370-43
CA1949
BAKELITE

$50

A54
CA1935
WOOD

$60

A52
CA1935
WOOD

$85

A62
CA1935
WOOD
OVERSIZED
TOMBSTONE

$125

A53
CA1935
WOOD

$75

A70
CA1936
WOOD
OVERSIZED
TOMBSTONE

$90

BX
CA1933
METAL
'LUNCHBOX'

$90

C751
(CANADA)
CA1941
PLASKON

$60

C122
(CANADA)
CA1940
BEETLE PLASTIC

$110

F40
CA1937
BAKELITE

$135

C415
CA1958
PLASTIC
CLOCK-RADIO

$30

F51
CA1937
BAKELITE

$135

F63
CA1937
WOOD

$90

GD60
CA1938
WOOD

$75

F81
CA1937
WOOD

$120

GD520
CA1939
BEETLE
BRASS FACE
PLATE

$350

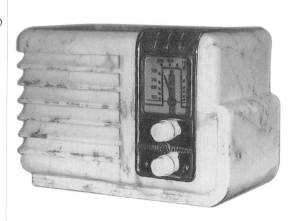

G64
CA1938
WOOD

$55

GD600
CA1939
WOOD

$45

GD610
CA1939
WOOD

$90

H530
CA1939
WOOD
MINI-
TOMBSTONE

$90

H500
CA1939
BAKELITE

$125

H600
CA1939

BEETLE $225

BROWN $65

IVORY $110

H510
CA1939

BEETLE $350

BROWN
$150

IVORY $225

HJ624
CA1039
WOOD
$90

K5OP

CA1934
WOOD

$175

L513

CA1941
WOOD

INLAID YELLOW
INGRAHAM
CABINET

$110

K53

CA1934
WOOD

$200

L542

CA1942
WOOD

INGRAHAM
CABINET

$50

KL53
(CANADA)
CA1939
WOOD

CHROME BARS
(VASSOS
ATTRIB.)

$175

L650

CA1941
BAKELITE

$80

L660
CA1942
WOOD
CHROME FACE
PLATE

$75

M40
CA1933
METAL
'LUNCHBOX'

$95

CA1938
WOOD
MINI-CONSOLE

$225

CA1940

IVORY
$125

BROWN
$75

CA1939

IVORY
$225

BROWN
$165

CA1940
BAKELITE

$150

CA1939

IVORY
$250

BROWN
$190

CA1947
MARBLED TENITE
W/PLASKON
TRIM

VARIOUS
COLORS
$275+

CA1947
BAKELITE
W/IVORY
PLASKON TRIM

$150

49
CA1947
WOOD
W/BAKELITE
TRIM

$90

A26
CA1948
WOOD
W/PLASKON
TRIM

$250

Grunow

CA1935
WOOD

$150

500
CA1934
WOOD
CHROME GRILLE

$250

420
CA1935
WOOD

$75

501
CA1934
WOOD
SILVER DETAIL
CHROME GRILLE

$135

450
CA1934
WOOD
CHROME GRILLE

$210

510
CA1935
WOOD
CHROME GRILLE

$150

520
CA1935
WOOD
BLACK LACQUER
DETAIL
CHROME GRILLE

$110

632
CA1936
WOOD
BRASS BEZEL &
TRIM

$85

542
CA1936
WOOD

$70

640
CA1936
WOOD

$125

588
CA1936
WOOD
BRASS BEZEL &
TRIM

$75

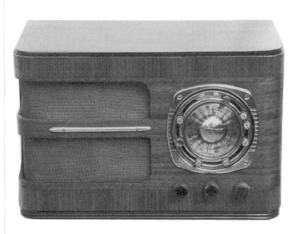

CA1934
WOOD
BLACK LACQUER
TRIM
CHROME DETAIL

$325

25
CA1937
WOOD

$50

'UNIVERSAL'
WOOD

$75

43BA
CA1933
WOOD
MARQUETRY

$175

O5
CA1935
WOOD

$65

5OX
CA1937
WOOD

$80

CA1933
WOOD
SILVER &
BLACK PAINT

$250

21
'MODERNE'
CLOCKETTE
CA1937
WOOD
BLACK
LACQUER TRIM

$150

CA1933
BAKELITE

$225

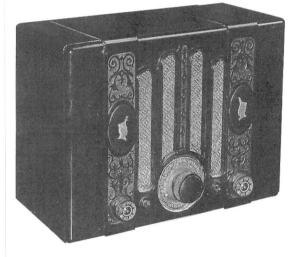

22
'COLONIAL'
CLOCKETTE
CA1937
WOOD

$125

CA1933
WOOD

$125

21
'SHERATON'
CLOCKETTE
CA1937
WOOD
LACEWOOD
VENEER

$125

KADETTE

32
CA1937
WOOD

$65

66
CA1936
WOOD

$75

35
CA1936
WOOD

$90

72
CA1936
WOOD

$200

48
'JEWEL'
CA1935
(NOS. 41-48)

MARBLED
$350+

BROWN $125

RED $300+

76
CA1936
WOOD

$75

77
CA1936
WOOD

$125

96
CA1937
WOOD

$45

86
CA1936
WOOD

$90

120
CA1937
WOOD

$150

87
CA1936
WOOD

$55

400
CA1936
WOOD

$120

KADETTE

500
CA1936
WOOD

$110

'JUNIOR'
CA1932
BAKELITE

BROWN
$125

PEANUT BUTTER
MARBLE
$200

RED
$750+

'CLASSIC'
CA1936
PLASKON,
TENITE

$750+

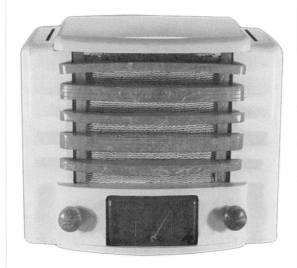

K150
CA1937
BAKELITE

PEANUT BUTTER
MARBLE
$225

BROWN
$150

'H'
CA1932

BEETLE
$350+

BAKELITE
$200

K739
CA1938
WOOD

$50

K1024
CA1938
WOOD

$65

KRC2
CA1937
WOOD
REMOTE
TUNER

$250

'TOPPER'
CA1940
BAKELITE,
PLASKON

$300

KNIGHT

2
CA11937
WOOD

$110

9503
CA1935
WOOD
BLACK LACQUER
DETAIL

$80

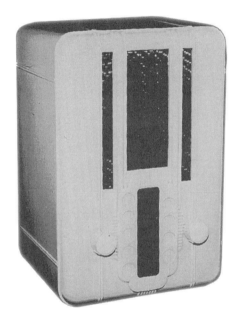

196AT
CA1940
PLASKON

$150

9547
CA1935
WOOD

$110

9501
CA1935
WOOD
2-TONE
LACQUER
INSERT GRILLE

$250

9621
CA1935
WOOD
BLACK LACQUER
DETAIL

$150

9633

CA1935
WOOD

$95

9707

CA1937
WOOD
2-TONE
LACQUER

$110

9700

CA1937
WOOD
BLACK LACQUER
DETAIL

$90

9710

CA1937
WOOD

$100

9701

CA1937
BAKELITE

$50

9720

CA1937
WOOD

$100

9744
CA1937
WOOD

$80

9803
CA1936
WOOD

$60

9775
CA1937
WOOD
BLACK LACQUER
DETAIL

$85

9803A
CA1936
WOOD

$130

9801
CA1936
WOOD
MARQUETRY
BLACK LACQUER
DETAIL

$120

9807
CA1936
WOOD

$100

9809

CA1936
WOOD
MARQUETRY

$75

9819

CA1936
WOOD

$80

9813

CA1936
WOOD

$65

9822

CA1936
WOOD

$90

9815

CA1936
WOOD

$90

9831

CA1936
WOOD

$110

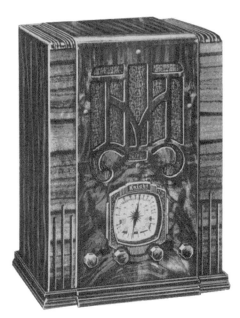

9835

CA1936
WOOD

$95

9851

CA1935
WOOD
'SKYSCRAPER'

$275

9837

CA1936
WOOD
TRAPEZOID
MARQUETRY
BLACK LACQUER
TRIM

$150

9852

CA1935
WOOD

$125

9843

CA1936
WOOD

$85

9853

CA1935
WOOD

$120

KNIGHT

9861

CA1935
WOOD
MARQUETRY

$95

9863

CA1935
WOOD
MARQUETRY
BLACK LACQUER
DETAIL

$90

9861A

CA1936
WOOD

$80

9864

CA1935
WOOD
BLACK LACQUER
DETAIL

$110

9862

CA1935
WOOD

$85

9865

CA1936
WOOD

$85

KNIGHT

9863

CA1936
WOOD

$110

9879

CA1935
WOOD

$100

9865

CA1936
WOOD

$95

9885

CA1935
WOOD

$95

9875

CA1935
WOOD
MARQUETRY

$85

9886

CA1936
WOOD
2-TONE
LACQUER

$125

9891
CA1935
WOOD

$95

10502
CA1938
BAKELITE

$80

9895
CA1935
WOOD

$90

10508
CA1938
WOOD

$100

10500
CA1938
WOOD
2-TONE
LACQUER

$70

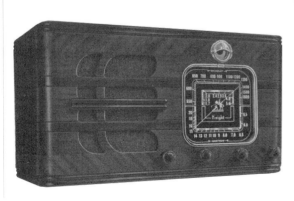

10508B
CA1941
PLASKON

$65

10509
CA1938
WOOD

$40

10516
CA1938
WOOD

$70

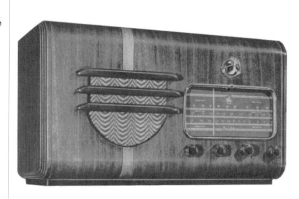

10510
CA1941
PLASKON

$65

10516A
CA1941
WOOD
2-TONE
LACQUER

$50

10514
CA1938
WOOD

$225

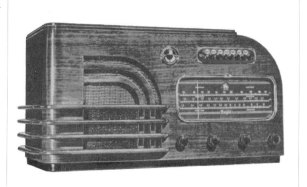

10517
CA1941
WOOD

$65

10518
CA1941
WOOD
2-TONE
LACQUER

$60

10535
CA1938
WOOD

$70

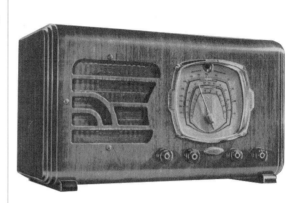

10530
CA1938
'3-POSITION'
BAKELITE
METAL TRIM

$175

10536
CA1941
BAKELITE

$65

10531
CA1941
BAKELITE

$70

10539
CA1941
WOOD

$50

10540
CA1938
WOOD

$90

10580
CA1938
WOOD

$90

10547
CA1938
WOOD

$70

10590
CA1938
WOOD

$85

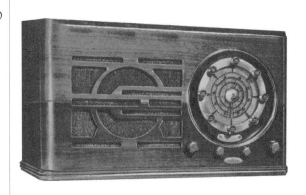

10555
CA1941
BEETLE

$250

10600
CA1938
WOOD

$85

CA1948
BAKELITE

$40

1R708
CA1948
BAKELITE

$40

1R413
CA1948
BAKELITE

$40

1R805
CA1948
BAKELITE

$45

1R521
CA1948
BAKELITE

$35

A23
CA1937
WOOD

$55

B14
CA1938
WOOD

$50

BB22
CA1940
BAKELITE

$250

B25
CA1938
WOOD

$90

BB27
CA1940
WOOD

$50

BA2
CA1938
WOOD

$65

BE78
CA1939
BAKELITE

$225

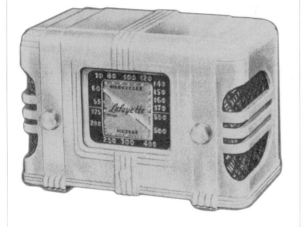

C3
CA1937

BLACK
BAKELITE
$125

IVORY
PLASKON
$175

RED
PLASKON
$350+

C65
CA1937
WOOD

$110

C21
CA1939
WOOD

$65

CC24
CA1939
BAKELITE

$65

C47
CA1937
WOOD

$90

CC29
CA1939
WOOD

$60

D22
CA1938
WOOD

$55

D34
CA1937
WOOD

$60

D32
CA1938
WOOD

$60

D36
CA1938
WOOD

$70

D33
CA1940
WOOD

$60

D38P
CA1937
WOOD

$60

D5O
CA1938
WOOD

$65

D73
CA1939
BAKELITE

$11O

D51
CA1938
WOOD

$125

D251
CA1942
WOOD

$45

D59
CA1939

IVORY
PLASKON
$2OO

BROWN
BAKELITE
$15O

DA11
CA1937
WOOD

$65

Lafayette

DA20
CA1937
WOOD

$60

E75
CA1939

IVORY
PLASKON
$160

BROWN
BAKELITE
$125

DA31
CA1937
WOOD

$70

E77
CA1939

IVORY
PLASKON
$75

BROWN
BAKELITE
$45

E63
CA1940
CATALIN

$1200+

EB15
CA1937
WOOD

$125

EB56
CA1938
WOOD

$70

FA10
CA1938

BLACK
BAKELITE
$350+

IVORY
PLASKON
$500+

RED
PLASKON
$1000+

EB66
CA1938
WOOD

$75

FE6
CA1940
BAKELITE

$110

EB67
CA1938
WOOD

$75

FE30
CA1940
WOOD

$40

FE35
CA1940
WOOD

$50

JA84
CA1940

IVORY
PLASKON
$85

BROWN
BAKELITE
$60

FS43
CA1937
WOOD

$50

JA93
CA1940

IVORY
PLASKON
$95

BROWN
BAKELITE
$70

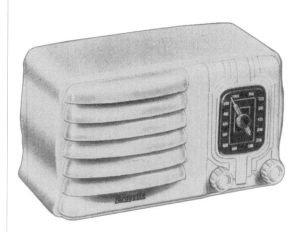

J50Y
CA1947
MARBLED
PLASTIC

$125

MC10Y
CA1947
BAKELITE

$60

CA1937
WOOD

$115

5AK711
CA1947
BAKELITE

$75

1A50A
CA1940
WOOD

$40

5CAA
CA1937
WOOD

$175

1A59
CA1940
WOOD

$45

5LA5
'ZEPHYR'
CA1939
BAKELITE

$110

5LA7
'ZEPHYR'
CA1937
BAKELITE

$100

7T11
CA1939
BAKELITE

$150

44
'DUO
CHIEF'
'SMART SET'
CA1933
WOOD
ALUMINIM
GRILLE &
ESCUTCHEONS

$110

49
'DUO
MODERN'
'SMART SET'
CA1933
WOOD
ALUMINIM
GRILLE &
ESCUTCHEONS
BLACK
LACQUER
TRIM

$250

51
CA1937

IVORY
PLASKON
$160

BROWN
BAKELITE
$125

54A
CA1934
WOOD
ALUMINIM
GRILLE &
ESCUTCHEONS

$275

55
'Duette'
'Smart Set'
CA1933
Wood
Aluminim
Grille &
Escutcheons

$250

75
CA1937
Wood

$200

59
'Studio'
'Smart Set'
CA1933
Wood
Aluminim
Grille &
Escutcheons
Black Lacquer
Trim

$425

76
CA1937
Wood

$175

66
CA1937
Wood

$90

104
CA1951
Ivory Plaskon

$500+

149
'SMART SET'
CA1934
WOOD
ALUMINIM
GRILLE &
ESCUTCHEONS
BLACK LACQUER
TRIM

$400

174
CA1934
WOOD
ALUMINUM
GRILLE
MOTORIZED
TIMER ON SIDE

$1000+

156
CA1936
WOOD
BLACK
LACQUER
TRIM

$85

196
'GOTHIC'
'SMART SET'
CA1933
WOOD

$225

161
CA1934
WOOD
CHROME GRILLE
& ESCUTCHEONS

$400

250MI
'ZEPHYR'
CA1939
BAKELITE

$135

370
CA1933
WOOD

$275

463
'CENTURY
SIX'
'SMART SET'
CA1933
WOOD
CHROME GRILLE
& ESCUTCHEONS

$175

411
'DELUXE'
'SMART SET'
CA1933
WOOD
ALUMINIM
GRILLE &
ESCUTCHEONS

$225

511
CA1937

BEETLE W/TENITE
TRIM
$400+

IVORY PLASKON
W/TENITE TRIM
$250

461
'MASTER
SIX'
'SMART SET'
CA1933
WOOD
CHROME
GRILLE &
ESCUTCHEONS

$160

651
CA1937
BAKELITE

$175

'CHARLIE'
CA1938

IVORY PLASKON
OR BLACK
BAKELITE

$900+

CA1940
IVORY PLASKON
GOLD & RED
GRILLE

$125

IS49
'MELODY
CRUISER'
CA1941

$350

'PETITE'
CA1939
WOOD

$135

CA1953
PLASTIC

$40

5T
CA1937
WOOD

$90

CA1955
PLASTIC

$75

5T21W1
CA1951
PLASTIC

$35

5L2U
CA1950
PLASTIC

$35

5T22M1
'DRAGSTER'
CA1951
PLASTIC

BROWN $65

BLACK $70

WHITE $70

YELLOW $90

RED $90

5X1U
CA1953
BAKELITE
w/METAL
STAND

$125

51A
CA1939
BAKELITE

$175

48L11
CA1948
2-TONE
PLASTIC

$40

51X11
CA1939
BAKELITE

$60

5OX1
CA1939
BAKELITE

$70

52R
CA1952
BAKELITE

$75

52X13U
CA1952
BAKELITE

$45

55X12
CA1946
BAKELITE

$50

53H
CA1954
BAKELITE

$125

56CD
CA1956
UREA
PASTEL COLORS

$110

53T2
CA1954
WOOD

$50

56H
'TURBINE'
CA1956
BAKELITE

$125

56R
CA1953
PLASTIC

$50

57X
CA1947
BAKELITE

$45

57H
CA1957
UREA
PASTEL COLORS

$90

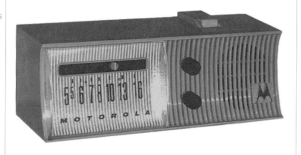

60AX
CA1939
BAKELITE

$115

57H1
CA1957
UREA
PASTEL COLORS

$80

63C
CA1954
BAKELITE

$75

67X
CA1947
BAKELITE

$70

161A
CA1939
BAKELITE

$135

69X
CA1950
BAKELITE

$60

FXFO1
CA1940
BAKELITE

$75

79XM21
CA1950
BAKELITE
w/CHROME

$80

7048
CA1940
WOOD

$65

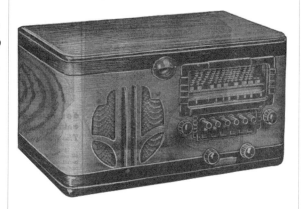

R3124
CA1941
BAKELITE

$40

C3-149
CA1941
WOOD

$85

R3126
CA1941
BAKELITE

$50

C3-151
CA1941
BAKELITE

$65

R3131
CA1941
WOOD

$50

CA1939
WOOD

$50

37-610
CA1937
WOOD

$110

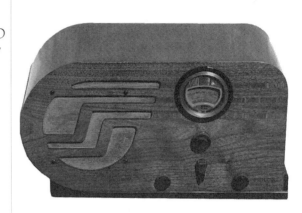

CA1939
BAKELITE &
PLASKON

$1200+

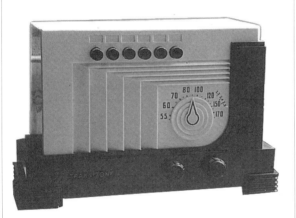

37-61OB
CA1937
WOOD

$75

CA1941
WOOD
'REFRIGERATOR'

$175

37-66OB
CA1937
WOOD

$135

PHILCO

37A
(CANADA)
CA1939
WOOD

$110

40-115
CA1940
WOOD

$60

38-9
CA1938
WOOD

$75

41-226
CA1941
WOOD
BLACK LACQUER

$125

38-62
CA1938
WOOD

$85

42-350
CA1942
WOOD

$125

42-KR5
CA1942
'REFRIGERATOR'
WOOD

$140

49-5O1
'BOOMERANG'
CA1949
BAKELITE

$275

45
'BUTTERFLY'
CA1934
WOOD
BLACK LACQUER

$175

49-5O3
'FLYING
WEDGE'
CA1949
PLASTIC

$150

47-9O2
CA1947
PLASTIC

$60

49-5O5
CA1949
BAKELITE

$90

PHILCO

49-506
'FLYING
WEDGE'
CA1949
WOOD &
PLASTIC

$75

50-526
CA1950
BAKELITE

$55

49-900
CA1949
BAKELITE

$45

51-538
CA1951
BAKELITE
CLOCK-RADIO

$50

49-901
'SECRETARY'
CA1949
BAKELITE

$175

52-940
CA1952
BAKELITE

$60

53-563
CA1953
BAKELITE

$75

54
CA1933
WOOD
2-TONE FINISH

$90

53-566
CA1953
BAKELITE

$125

610
CA1936
WOOD

$120

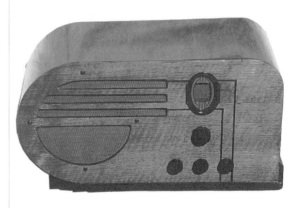

53-706
CA1953
WOOD
RADIO-LAMP

$140

640
CA1936
WOOD

$110

PHILCO

PT27
CA1940
BAKELITE

$45

PT49
CA1939
WOOD

$85

PT43
CA1939
WOOD
TENITE GRILLE &
TRIM

$125

PT61
CA1940
WOOD

$100

PT46
CA1939
BAKELITE

$75

PT65
CA1940
WOOD

$60

PT67
CA1940
BAKELITE
TENITE GRILLE
& TRIM

$175

TH7
CA1939
BAKELITE

$75

PT69
CA1940
WOOD
CLOCK-RADIO

$110

TP7
'COLLEGE'
CA1939
BAKELITE
TENITE GRILLE
& TRIM

$190

T1000-124
'PREDICTA'
CA1959
PLASTIC

$150

'TRANSITONE'
CA1949
MARBLED
PLASTIC

$50

CA1936
WOOD

$250

93
CA1934
WOOD
MARQUETRY

$150

200
CA1936

BAKELITE
w/GOLD
TRIM
$400

IVORY
PLASKON
$750+

'JUNIOR'
CA1940
IVORY
PLASKON
W/BLACK
GRILLE INSERTS

$350

250
CA1936
WOOD

$325

'MAJOR
MAESTRO'
CA1947
BAKELITE

$125

4X
CA1936
WOOD
MINI-
TOMBSTONE

$135

4X55
CA1955
PLASTIC
(RED, WHITE,
BROWN, BLACK)

$75

4X3
CA1936
WOOD
MINI-
TOMBSTONE

$135

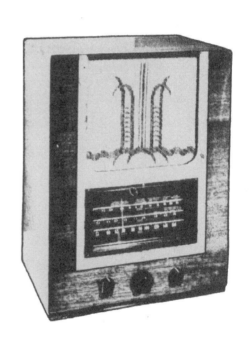

5Q2X
CA1940
WOOD

$60

4X4
CA1936
WOOD
MINI-
TOMBSTONE

$115

5Q55
CA1939
BAKELITE
(VASSOS
ATTR.)

$50

5T
CA1936
WOOD

$110

5T8
CA1936
WOOD

$110

5T1
CA1936
WOOD

$125

5X
CA1937
WOOD

$115

5T7
CA1936
WOOD

$110

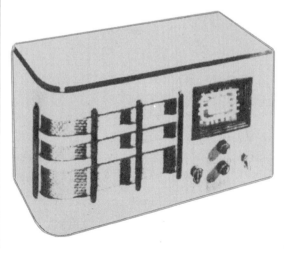

5X2
CA1937
WOOD

$125

5X3
CA1937
WOOD

$95

6T1O
CA1936
(VASSOS DES.)
WOOD
CHROME
STAND & TRIM

$1000+

5X5
CA1939
BAKELITE

$60

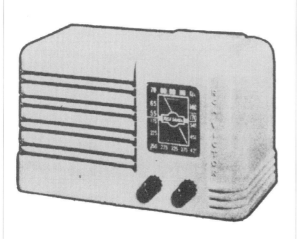

7T
CA1936
WOOD

$150

6Q8
CA1940
WOOD

$75

8Q4
CA1940
WOOD
CHROME TRIM

$150

7T1
ca1936
Wood

$130

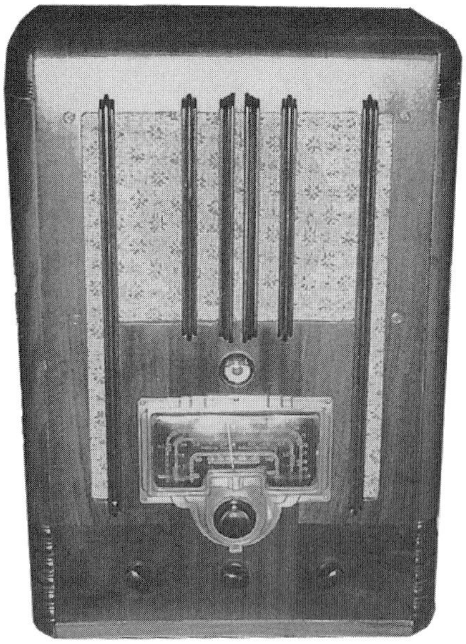

8T10
ca1936
(Vassos Des.)
Wood
Chrome
Stand &
Trim
Black Lacquer

$1000+

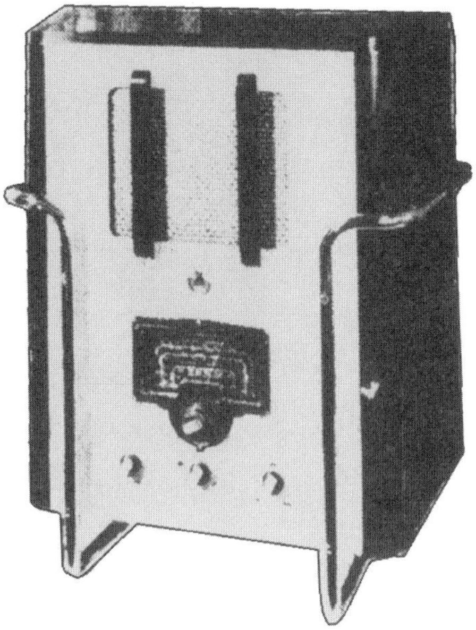

8X54
ca1948
Bakelite

$65

RCA VICTOR

9SX
ca1934

Beetle Grille
Plaskon Body
$750+

Bakelite
$250

RCA VICTOR

9T
ca1935
Wood

$150

9TX
ca1939

Brown
$100

Ivory
$175

9TX3
CA1939
WOOD

$150

9TX23
CA1939
WOOD

$150

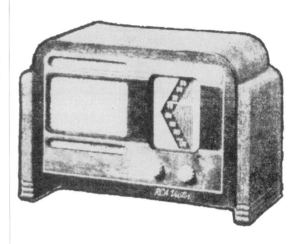

9TX4
CA1939
CATALIN

$1100+

9TX50
CA1939
WOOD

$110

9TX21
CA1939
BAKELITE

$60

9X6
CA1939
WOOD

$100

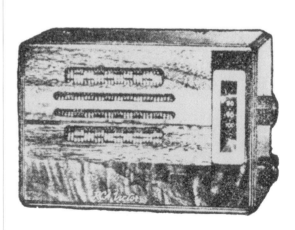

1OT1
CA1936
WOOD

$175

4OX53
'LA SIESTA'
CA1939

WOOD
HAND-
PANTED

$600

16T4
CA1940
WOOD

$70

4OX54
'TREASURE
CHEST'
CA1939
WOOD

$375

4OX50
CA1939
WOOD

$110

4OX55
CA1939
WOOD

$110

40X57
'SF Expo'
CA1939
Repwood

$1200+

46X24
CA1940
Wood

$55

46X13
CA1940
Wood

$50

85T8
CA1938
Wood
Black Lacquer

$100

46X21
CA1940
Bakelite

$40

86T3
CA1938
Wood

$80

87T
CA1938
WOOD

$60

94X
CA1938
WOOD
2-TONE
LACQUER

$95

91B
CA1933
METAL
'LUNCHBOX'
SILVER &
BLACK PAINT

$115

94X1
CA1938
WOOD

$75

94BT1
CA1938
WOOD
BLACK LACQUER

$100

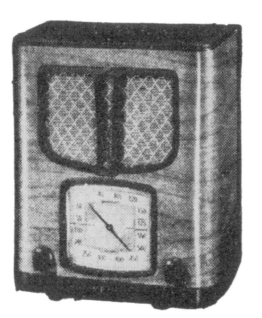

95T
CA1938
WOOD
$125

95T5
CA1938
WOOD

$50

95XL
CA1938

$250

95X
CA1938
WOOD

$65

96T1
CA1938
WOOD
INGRAHAM
CABINET

$125

95X1
CA1938
WOOD

$95

96TZ
CA1939
WOOD
CHROME BARS &
TRIM

$90

96X13
CA1939
(VASSOS DES.)

BROWN &
TAN
$400

BROWN
$275

IVORY
$325

101
CA1933
WOOD

$150

98X
CA1938
WOOD
BLACK
LACQUER
TRIM

$85

110
CA1933
WOOD

$225

100
CA1933
WOOD

$185

111
CA1933
WOOD

$110

115
CA1933
WOOD

$150

120
CA1933
WOOD

$225

117
CA1934
WOOD

$150

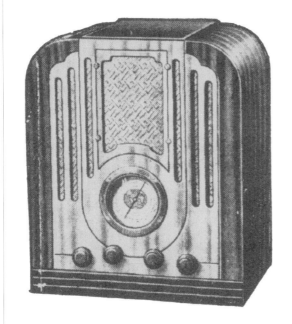

121
CA1934
WOOD

$250

119
CA1934
WOOD
2-TONE
LACQUER

$125

122
CA1934
WOOD

$165

124
CA1935
WOOD
REPWOOD
GRILLE

$275

143
CA1934
WOOD

$350

140
CA1934
WOOD

$275

228P
CA1933
WOOD

$225

141
CA1934
WOOD
BLACK LACQUER

$275

301
CA1933
WOOD

$110

806
CA1936
WOOD

$90

A2O
(CANADA)
CA1939
WOOD
CHROME FINS
(VASSOS ATTRIB.)

$325

811T
CA1937
WOOD

$95

R22S
CA1933
REPWOOD

$200

812X
CA1937
WOOD

$120

T8-18
CA1935
WOOD

$145

CA1939
WOOD

$75

R201U
CA1955
PLASTIC

$60

313
CA1935
WOOD

$250

R636
CA1933
WOOD

$225

4511
CA1934
WOOD
ALUMINUM
ESCUTCHEONS
BLACK LACQUER
MARQUETRY

$225

R861
CA1933
WOOD

$275

CA1938
WOOD

$65

137BT

CA1939
BAKELITE

$100

60BT

CA1937
WOOD

$70

195ULTO

CA1939
BEETLE

$350

118BT

CA1938
BAKELITE

$55

218

CA1947
BAKELITE

$70

Sentinel

284IN
CA1947
CATALIN

$800+

'TREASURE
CHEST'
CA1947
PLASTIC

$110

3091
CA1947
BAKELITE

$65

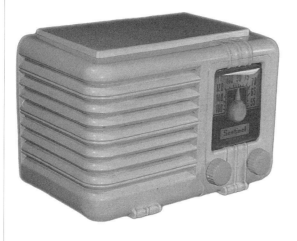

314W
CA1948
BAKELITE

$50

58A-375
'Jet'
ca1949
Wood

$500+

485R
ca1948
Black Bakelite
Radio-
Intercom

$125

416
'Frog-Eye'
ca1946
Plastic

Brown $70
Ivory $90
Red $135
Blue $175

570
'Cylinder'
ca1948
Reverse-
Painted Mylar
w/Wood or
Plastic Ends
Removeable
Pillow Speaker
(Black,
Orange,
Yellow,
White, Red,
etc.)

$250+

427
'Big Frog-
Eye'
ca1947
Plastic

Brown $65
Ivory $80
Red $125
Blue $175

SILVERTONE

CA1937
WOOD
BLACK LACQUER

$90

4
'COWBOY'
CA1951
BLACK & WHITE
PLASTIC

$350+

CA1949
BAKELITE

$75

132.804
CA1939
BAKELITE

$75

1
CA1950
METAL MIDGET
(ARVIN)

$45

132.838
CA1950
BAKELITE

$55

1704
CA1933
WOOD
COLOR INLAY

$80

1906
CA1935
WOOD
2-TONE
LACQUER

$110

1805
CA1935
WOOD
MARQUETRY

$125

1938
CA1935
WOOD
2-TONE
LACQUER

$90

1904
CA1935
WOOD
2-TONE
LACQUER

$90

2001
CA1950
METAL MIDGET
(ARVIN)

$65

SILVERTONE

3061
CA1940

BEETLE
W//TAN,
GREEN OR BLUE
MARBLED
TENITE TRIM
$250+

BAKELITE
wTENITE TRIM
$150

4500
'ELECTION'
CA1936

BLACK BAKELITE
$125

IVORY PLASKON
$150

LAVENDER
PLASKON
$1000+

3551
'CANDY-
CANE'
CA1940

BEETLE
$225

BAKELITE
$80

4565
CA1937
WOOD
$110

4403
CA1937
WOOD

$75

4660
CA1938
WOOD

$125

4763

CA1938
WOOD

$110

6050

CA1940
WOOD
METAL GRILLE

$60

487F

CA1938
WOOD

$90

6106

CA1939

RED PLASKON
$500+

IVORY PLASKON
$200

BLACK BAKELITE
$150

BROWN BAKELITE
$135

6002

CA1937

BLACK BAKELITE
$135

IVORY PLASKON
$160

6110

'ROCKET'
CA1938

BLACK BAKELITE
$750+

IVORY PLASKON
$1200+

SILVERTONE

6120

CA1939

WOOD

INGRAHAM
CABINET

$250

6319

CA1939

BROWN
BAKELITE
$125

BLACK BAKELITE
$150

6178

'BULLET'

CA1939

IVORY PLASKON
$225

BLACK BAKELITE
$200

BROWN BAKELITE
$175

6320

CA1939

WOOD

COPPER
FACEPLATE

$200

6230

CA1939

WOOD

INGRAHAM
CABINET

$175

6402

CA1939

BAKELITE

$175

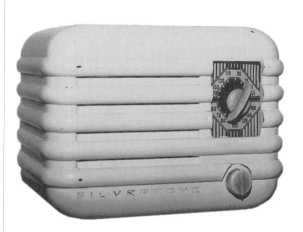

6405

CA1939

BROWN BAKELITE
$135

BLACK BAKELITE
$150

BEETLE
$350

7020

CA1949
METAL
(ARVIN)

$125

6406

CA1939
WOOD

$165

8010

CA1949
PLASTIC

$50

7000

CA1949

BEETLE
$250

BAKELITE
$75

8217

CA1949
2-TONE
PLASTIC

$110

SILVERTONE

9000
CA1950
BAKELITE

$45

'WEDGE'
CA1959
PLASTIC

$50

9005
CA1950
BAKELITE

$40

'CORONET'
CA1937
BAKELITE

$500+

CA1939
BEETLE
$225

IVORY
PLASKON
$150

100
CA1946
BAKELITE

$40

CA1941
WOOD

$45

A11
'PETER PAN'
CA1939
BAKELITE

$60

CA1946
BAKELITE

$45

'BROWNIE'
CA1948
BAKELITE
CAMERA-RADIO

$125

C22
CA1939
IVORY PLASKON
& BLACK
BAKELITE

$95

LKSU180
CA1939
WOOD
INGRAHAM
CABINET

$125

'CAMEO'
CA1941
WOOD

$60

P99
'TEENY
WEENY'
CA1939
WOOD

$125

D12
CA1939
WOOD
INGRAHAM
CABINET

$80

P106
CA1939
BAKELITE

$85

RCU206
CA1939
WOOD
INGRAHAM
CABINET

$110

TW49
CA1939

BROWN BAKELITE
$275

BLACK BAKELITE
$300

BEETLE
$450+

RDAU209
CA1940
WOOD
INGRAHAM
CABINET

$110

WEU240
CA1948
BAKELITE

$75

TS105
'COSMO'
CA1939
BAKELITE

$65

WJU252
CA1942
BAKELITE
VARIOUS COLOR
COMBINATIONS

$125

CA1933
WOOD
MARQUETRY

$100

CA1939
(CANADA)
BROWN BAKELITE
MARBLED TENITE
GRILLE

$350

CA1934
(CANADA)
WOOD

$225

CA1940
(CANADA)
BROWN BAKELITE
MARBLED TENITE
GRILLE

$325

CA1936
(CANADA)
WOOD

$225

6-66A
CA1946
WOOD
2-TONE
LACQUER

$60

53
CA1934
WOOD
MARQUETRY

$90

508
CA1935
WOOD

$175

500DG
CA1938
WOOD MIDGET
INGRAHAM
CABINET

$110

517B
CA1936
WOOD
BLACK LACQUER
& CHROME

$450+

507
CA1935
WOOD
CHROME TRIM

$350

537
CA1937
WOOD

$175

616
CA1935
WOOD
BLACK LACQUER
CROWN

$300

'LOBSTER'
CA1940
WOOD
INGRAHAM
CABINET

$325

5149
(CANADA)
CA1939
WOOD

$90

'POLO'
CA1939
BAKELITE
RELIEF OF POLO
PLAYER ON TOP

BROWN BAKELITE
$325
BLACK BAKELITE
$375
IVORY PLASKON
$450
RED PLASKON
$1000+

'CLOISONNE'
CA1939
CATALIN
W/METAL
GRILLE

$2500+

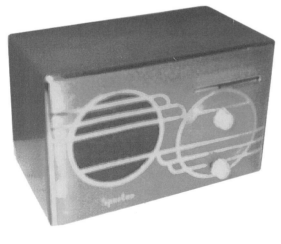

'SUNRISE'
CA1934

$150

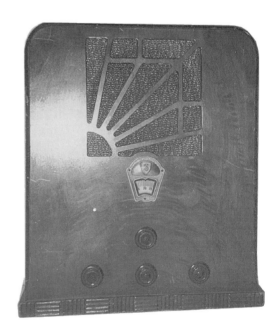

CA1934
'FERRODYNE'
WOOD

$150

O3-5S2
CA1939
WOOD

$110

CA1937
WOOD

$75

O7-512
'CAMPUS
CA1949

IVORY PLASKON
$200

BROWN BAKELITE
$110

CA1939
3-POSITION
WOOD

$110

O7-5B
'SENIOR
VARSITY'
CA1939
BAKELITE
VARIOUS
COLLEGE COLOR
COMBINATIONS

$300

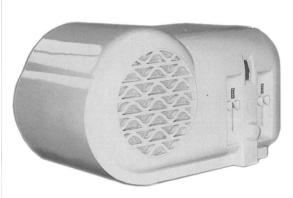

O7-5R4
CA1940
WOOD
INGRAHAM
CABINET

$135

91-621
CA1940
WOOD
INGRAHAM
CABINET

$200

11-62
CA1940
WOOD
INGRAHAM
CABINET

$175

97-52
CA1940
WOOD
BLACK LACQUER
& CHROME TRIM

$200

13-6P
CA1940
WOOD

$90

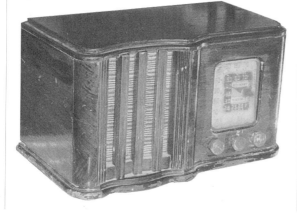

206FA
CA1941
BAKELITE

$60

1231
'Troubador'
ca1933
Wood

$250

1252
'Berkley'
ca1933
Wood
Black Lacquer

$225

1235
'Aristocrat'
ca1933
Wood
Chrome Grille

$325

1261
'York'
ca1933
Wood

$375+

1251
'Strand'
ca1933
Wood

$325

1262
'Stuart'
ca1933
Wood

$450+

1271
'BOND'
CA1933
WOOD

$300

1441
CA1936
WOOD

$90

1272
'PRADO'
CA1933
WOOD

$225

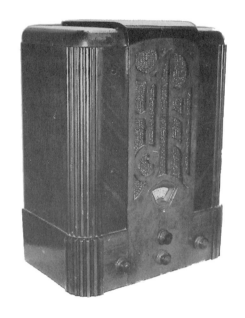

1721
CA1937
WOOD

$100

1421
CA1936
WOOD

$165

9000B
CA1940
WOOD
CHROME GRILLE

$65

A51T3
'AIR PAL'
CA1947
BAKELITE

$80

B51J
'AIR PAL'
CA1948
BAKELITE

$80

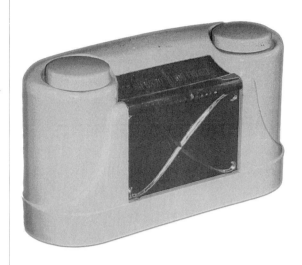

A6S
'AIR PAL'
CA1939
BAKELITE

$125

CENTURY
OF
PROGRESS
CA1933
PRESSWOOD
GOLD &
BRONZE

$300+

A72T1
CA1948
BAKELITE

$75

CENTURY
OF
PROGRESS
CA1933
WOOD
GOLD METAL
GRILLE

$350+

CENTURY
OF
PROGRESS
CA1933
PRESSBOARD
GOLD & BRONZE

$350+

R110
CA1934
WOOD

$275

R108
CENTURY
OF
PROGRESS
CA1933
METAL
W/DECALS

$300

R115
'COMPANION'
CA1933
WOOD

$90

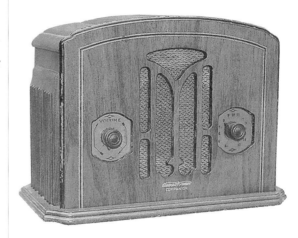

R108A
CA1934
METAL

$150

R140
CA1934
WOOD

$175

R167A
CA1936
WOOD

$115

R469
CA1940
WOOD
INGRAHAM
CABINET

$160

R172A
CA1935
WOOD

$110

R1302
CA1934
'FERRODYNE'
WOOD

$175

R247A
CA1935
WOOD

$150

R3044A
CA1939
WOOD
GREEN
LACQUER
TRIM

$225

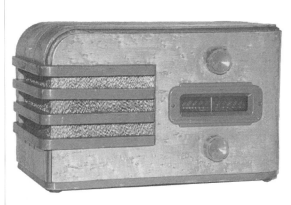

60
CA1934
WOOD

$150

61U
CA1935
WOOD

$175

61H
CA1935
WOOD

$125

125H
CA1936
WOOD

$150

61T
CA1935
WOOD

$125

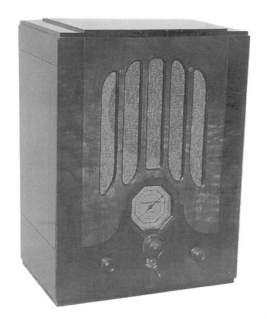

127
CA1936
WOOD

$150

130H
CA1936
WOOD

$125

140H
CA1936
WOOD

$175

130R
CA1936
WOOD

$150

225H
CA1937
WOOD
BLACK LACQUER
DETAIL

$250

130U
CA1936
WOOD

$350+

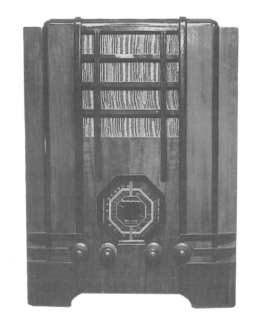

228H
CA1937
WOOD

$135

230H
CA1937
WOOD

$175

335H
CA1939
WOOD

$100

240H
CA1937
WOOD
BLACK LACQUER
DETAIL

$225

405H
CA1939
WOOD

$75

320H
CA1938
WOOD

$60

410J
CA1939
WOOD

$60

420H
CA1939
WOOD

$80

600H
CA1941
BAKELITE

$45

500J
CA1940
WOOD

$75

761
CA1941
BAKELITE

$50

500S
CA1940
WOOD

$175

900H
CA1941
BAKELITE

$50

1000J
CA1941
WOOD
INGRAHAM
CABINET

$150

1500H
CA1951
BAKELITE

BROWN
$50

MAROON
$85

1110H
CA1941
WOOD
INGRAHAM
CABINET

$150

C1
CA1951
PLASTIC

$40

1204
CA1948
BAKELITE
METAL GRILLE

$50

C3
CA1955
PLASTIC

$40

CA1936
WOOD

$70

CA1937
WOOD

$75

CA1936
WOOD
BLACK LACQUER
TRIM

$110

CA1947
BAKELITE

$45

CA1937
WOOD

$100

41
CA1935
WOOD

$125

315
CA1939
WOOD
BLACK LACQUER
TRIM

$300

5060
CA1950
BAKELITE

$70

442
CA1936
WOOD

$325+

T203
CA1959
PLASTIC

$75

5051
CA1948
BAKELITE

$45

CA1935
WOOD
MARQUETRY

$150

404
CA1938
WOOD

$175

CA1938
BAKELITE
CHROME GRILLE

$225

636
CA1938
BAKELITE

$135

278-5Q
'STRATO-
SCOPE'
CA1939

BEETLE
$350

BAKELITE
$175

9052
CA1947
BAKELITE

$50

D723

CA1936
WOOD

$80

D1014

CA1940
WOOD
INGRAHAM
CABINET

$75

D731

CA1938
BAKELITE

$125

D2018

'BOOMERANG'
CA1950
BAKELITE

$175

D1013

CA1941
WOOD
INGRAHAM
CABINET
RED MARBLED
PLASTIC
ESCUTCHEON

$75

D2210

CA1941
(TEAGUE DES.)
WOOD-
GRAINED
METAL
CHROME GRILLE

$125

D2661
CA1946
BAKELITE

$125

D2716
CA1947
(BELMONT)
BAKELITE

$90

'JR.'
CA1939
BAKELITE

$135

CA1949
(CANADA)
PLASTIC

$45

576
(CANADA)
CA1940
BAKELITE W/RED
PLASKON TRIM

$75

54
(CANADA)
CA1934
WOOD

$225

577
(CANADA)
CA1941
WOOD

$65

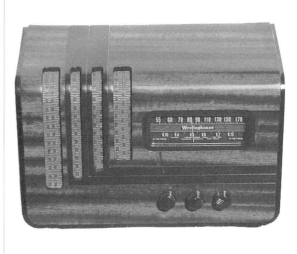

471B
(CANADA)
CA1939
WOOD

$80

H125
'LITTLE
JEWEL'
CA1948
BAKELITE

$100

H204
CA1948
BAKELITE

$75

H398T5
CA1955
PLASTIC

$60

H31OT5
CA1950
PLASTIC

$40

H418T5
CA1954
PLASTIC

$70

H32OT5
CA1950
PLASTIC

$50

H648T4
CA1958
PLASTIC

$40

WR011
CA1934
WOOD
INGRAHAM
CABINET

$100

WR100
CA1935
REPWOOD

$200

WR101
CA1935
WOOD

$165

WR166
CA1938
BAKELITE

$90

WR100
CA1935
REPWOOD

$200

WR175
CA1940
BAKELITE

$65

WR203
CA1935
WOOD

$150

WR211
CA1936
WOOD

$95

WR209
CA1936
WOOD

$75

WR212
CA1936
WOOD

$90

WR210
CA1936
WOOD

$75

WR214
CA1936
WOOD

$225

CA1935
WOOD
BLACK LACQUER
DEATIL

$175

A16
CA1937
WOOD

$75

5A675
CA1935
WOOD
BLACK LACQUER
DEATIL

$175

A17
CA1937
WOOD
BLACK LACQUER
FINISH

$1200+

A15
CA1937
WOOD
BLACK METAL
GRILLE

$225

A31
CA1938
WOOD
BLACK
LACQUER RIBS

$200

A35

CA1938
WOOD

$160

'THIN
MAN'
CA1937

BAKELITE
$225

IVORY PLASKON
$300

GREEN PLASKON
$400+

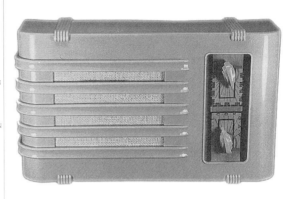

A46

CA1938
WOOD
BLACK METAL
GRILLES

$125

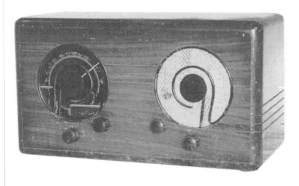

A52

CA1938
WOOD
2-TONE
LACQUER

$80

4K600
CA1941
BAKELITE &
CHROME

$110

6D030
CA1946
WOOD

$60

5A10
CA1946
WOOD

$135

27
CA1936
WOOD

$200

6D015
CA1946
BAKELITE

$50

29
CA1936
WOOD

$175

30

CA1936
WOOD

$700+

117

CA1937
WOOD
2-TONE
LACQUER

$110

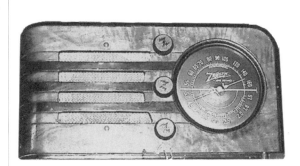

31

CA1936
WOOD
BLACK LACQUER
DETAIL

$125

119

CA1937
WOOD

$100

116

CA1937
WOOD

$90

126

CA1937
WOOD

$150

127
CA1937
WOOD

$225

130
CA1937
WOOD

$700+

128
CA1937
WOOD

$250

131
CA1937
WOOD

$115

129
CA1937
WOOD

$225

136
CA1937
WOOD

$100

137
'ZEPHYR'
CA1937
WOOD

$650+

226
CA1938
WOOD

$275

216
CA1938
WOOD

$135

228
CA1938
WOOD
BLACK LACQUER
DETAIL

$250

218
CA1938
WOOD

$150

229
CA1939
WOOD
'PAPER' FINISH

$150

232
'WALTON'
CA1938

7-TUBE
$900

9-TUBE
$1000

12-TUBE
$1200

312
CA1939
BAKELITE

$135

310
CA1939
BAKELITE

$125

312
CA1939
WOOD

$225

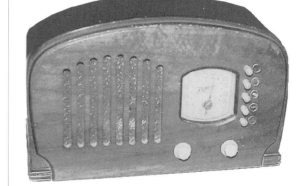

311
'WAVE-
MAGNET'
CA1939
BAKELITE

$150

314
CA1939
BAKELITE

$150

317
'Glass Rod'
CA1939
Wood
w/Glass &
Gold Rods

$300

321
CA1939
Wood

$165

319
CA1939
Wood

$125

326
CA1939
Wood

$225

320
CA1939
Wood

$140

327
CA1939
Wood

$500+

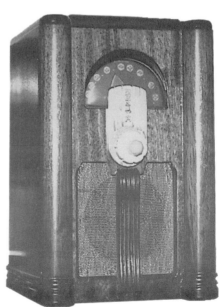

410
CA1940
BAKELITE

$110

428
CA1940
WOOD

$150

413
CA1940
BAKELITE

$150

429
CA1940
WOOD

$175

425
CA1940
WOOD

$125

430
CA1940
WOOD

$375+

432
CA1940
WOOD

$135

511
CA1941
BAKELITE

$50

439
CA1940
WOOD

$80

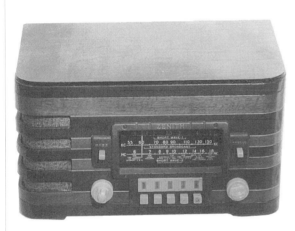

512
CA1941
BAKELITE

$85

481
CA1940
WOOD
RADIO-PHONE

$400

525
CA1941
WOOD

$110

526
CA1941
WOOD
INGRAHAM
CABINET

$150

538
CA1941
WOOD

$110

528
CA1941
WOOD
INGRAHAM
CABINET

$125

615
CA1942
BAKELITE

$55

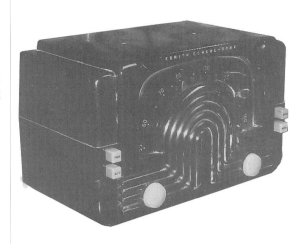

531
CA1941
WOOD

$125

628
CA1942
WOOD

$110

701
CHALLENGER
SERIES
CA1934
WOOD

$110

715
CA1934
WOOD

$275

707
CHALLENGER
SERIES
CA1934
WOOD
MARQUETRY
INLAID
'IVORY'
BLACK LACQUER
DETAIL

$250

801
CA1935
WOOD

$125

711
CHALLENGER
SERIES
CA1934
WOOD

$150

807
CA1935
WOOD

$150

808

CA1935
WOOD

$225

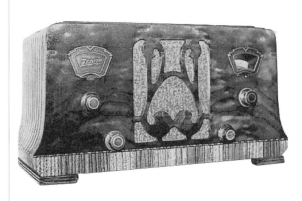

825

CA1935
WOOD

$165

809

CA1935
WOOD
CHROME GRILLE

$700+

829

CA1935
WOOD
CHROME GRILLE

$700+

811

CA1935
WOOD

$650+

835

CA1935
WOOD
CHROME GRILLE

$1000+

A515V
CA1958
BLACK PLASTIC
RED GRILLE

$50

H511V
CA1955
RED
PLASTIC

$45

G516
CA1950
BAKELITE

$45

J616
CA1952
BAKELITE

$35

H511
CA1951
BAKELITE

$60

J733
CA1952

$40

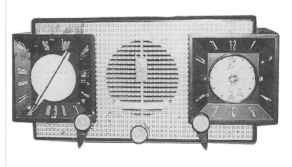

223

K412R
'CREST'
CA1953
BAKELITE
GOLD TRIM

$125

M403
CA1952
BAKELITE

$45

'ZENETTE'
CA1953
PLASTIC

$45

ABBOTTWARE

Z477
CA1950
METAL

$225

AETNA

CA1939
IVORY PLASKON

$125

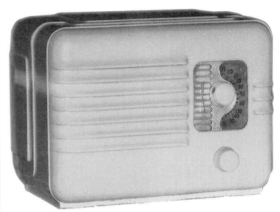

AETNA

CA1937
BAKELITE

$125

AETNA

400
CA1935

$110

AETNA

CA1937
WOOD
BLACK LACQUER
DETAIL

$150

AIRITE

'DESK SET'
CA1937
BAKELITE

$500+

American Bosch

CA1934
Wood

$150

Arkay

CA1948
Bakelite

$45

American Bosch

376BT
CA1933
Wood

$90

Auburn

CA1933
Wood

$75

American Bosch

660T
CA1937
Wood

$75

Automatic

601
CA1947
Bakelite

$90

AUTOMATIC

612X
CA1948
WOOD

$100

BERKSHIRE

CA1933
WOOD
2-TONE
LACQUER

$75

AUTOMATIC

614X
CA1948
BAKELITE

$65

BEST

'BULLET'
CA1937
WOOD

$150

BALKEIT

70
'ROUND
THE
WORLD'
CA1934

$325

BEST

CA1937
WOOD
2-TONE
LACQUER

$60

Miscellaneous

Black Hawk

ca1937
Wood
Marquetry

$75

Cabana

ca1948
Plastic

$40

Bulova

100
ca1957
Plastic

$50

Channel Master

6511
ca1959
Plastic

$45

Bulova

300
ca1958
Plastic

$50

Chesterfield

ca1936
Wood
2-Tone
Lacquer

$150

CHRYSLER

CA1936
WOOD

$110

CLARION

CA1940
WOOD

$50

CLARION

CA1934
WOOD

$60

CLARION

400
CA1933
WOOD

$75

CLARION

CA1939
WOOD

$250

CLINTON

CA1935
METAL

$90

MISCELLANEOUS

CLINTON

CA1937
WOOD

$65

CONTINENTAL

1600
CA1948
PLASTIC

$125

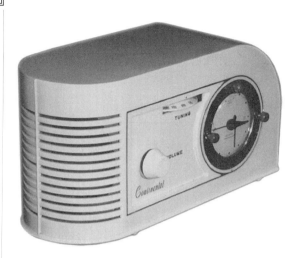

CLINTON

CA1937
WOOD

$85

CRUSADER

CA1936
WOOD

$70

CLINTON

53
CA1936
WOOD

$60

CUNNINGHAM

CA1937
WOOD
MINI-CONSOLE

$225

DAHLBERG

413OD
CA1955
PLASTIC
COIN-OP

$150

DUMONT

CA1956
PLASTIC

$125

DEFOREST
(CANADA)

CA1934
(ROGERS)
WOOD

$175

ELECTONE

CA1947
METAL

$60

DEFOREST
(CANADA)

CA1936
WOOD

$175

ELECTRONIC

CA1948
BAKELITE

$50

MISCELLANEOUS

CA1948
BAKELITE

$50

ERLA

72AT
CA1937
WOOD

$50

EMPIRE

CA1935
WOOD

$125

ERLA

289
CA1936
WOOD

$110

EPSE

31
'ROUND-
ABOUT'
CA1950
PLASTIC

$350

FAIRBANKS
-MORSE

58T1
CA1937
WOOD

$120

FAIRBANKS
-MORSE

58T2
CA1937
WOOD

$100

FEDERAL

746
CA1937
WOOD

$50

FAIRBANKS
-MORSE

69T7
CA1937
WOOD

$70

FRESHMAN

CA1938
WOOD

$55

FEDERAL

CA1938
LAVENDER &
BLACK PLASKON

$500+

FRESHMAN

426
CA1933
WOOD
ALUMINUM
GRILLE

$275

MISCELLANEOUS

GAROD

1B551
'COMMANDER'
CA1940
CATALIN

$1200+

GLOBE

'JUMBO
JUNIOR'
GENERAL
TIRE
PROMO
CA1947

$500+

GAROD

5A2
CA1946
BAKELITE

$85

GLOBE

'TROTTER'
CA1937

$750+

GAROD

307L
CA1938
WOOD

$90

GLORITONE

398-6M
CA1940
BEETLE

$275

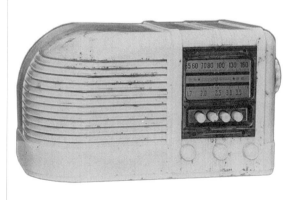

GOODYEAR

CA1939
BAKELITE

$190

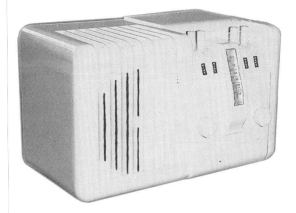

GRIDIRON

'GRIDIRON'
CA1948
PLASTIC

$500+

GREBE

206L
CA1938
WOOD

$125

GUILD

'TREASURE
CHEST'
CA1959
WOOD

$200

GREBE

5140
CA1937
WOOD

$175

HETRO

18810
CA1937
WOOD

$90

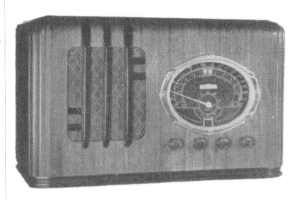

MISCELLANEOUS

HI-LO

CA1934
WOOD
MARQUETRY

$90

HOWARD

CA1937
WOOD
BLACK LACQUER
DETAIL

$125

HOLLYWOOD

'NAVIGATOR'
CA1948
WOOD

$300

IMPERIAL

CA1936
WOOD
MARQUETRY
BLACK LACQUER
DETAIL

$150

HOTEL RADIO

CA1949
METAL
COIN-OP

$75

IMPERIAL

6M27
CA1937
WOOD

$80

IMPERIAL

614
CA1936
WOOD

$200

JACKSON
BELL

CA1935
WOOD

$110

JACKSON
BELL

25
'PETER PAN'
CA1933
WOOD

$350+

KENT

422
CA1941
METAL MIDGET

$90

JACKSON
BELL

84
'PETER PAN'
CA1934
WOOD
BLACK LACQUER
SILHOUETTE
INSERT

$500+

LEWOL

CA1933
WOOD

$225

MISCELLANEOUS

LIBERTYTONE

CA1936
MIRROR

$750+

LYRIC

546T
CA1947
BAKELITE

$50

LIONEL

CA1940
(PILOT)
IVORY PLASKON

$325

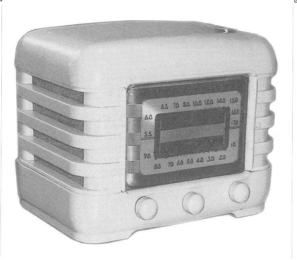

LYRIC

U55
CA1933
WOOD
2-TONE
LACQUER

$75

LTATRO

CA1936
WOOD

$100

MAGUIRE

CA1948
BAKELITE

$45

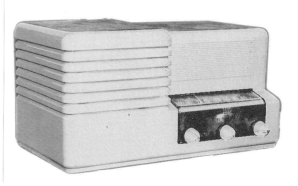

MANTOLA

CA1939
IVORY
PLASKON
GOLD METAL
TRIM

$225

MARCONI
(CANADA)

CA1935
WOOD
CHROME BARS

$350

MANTOLA

CA1939
BAKELITE

$175

MARCONI
(CANADA)

CA1936
WOOD

$175

MANTOLA

477-5LQ
CA1939
BAKELITE

$135

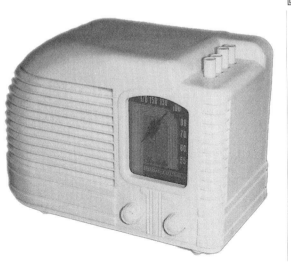

MARCONI
(CANADA)

CA1937
WOOD

$90

MISCELLANEOUS

MARCONI (CANADA)

126
CA1939
WOOD

$80

MECK

4C7
CA1947
PLASTIC

$60

MARCONI (CANADA)

218
CA1941
BAKELITE

$90

MECK

DB602
CA1948
PLASTIC

$50

MCCRORY

76-1
'CLASSIC'
CA1948
WOOD

$60

MELBURNE

CA1934
WOOD
CHROME
HANDLE
BLACK LACQUER
TRIM

$90

MEL-O-TONE

CA1934
WOOD

$75

MIDWEST

CA1939
WOOD

$225

MERIDIAN

237
CA1947
WOOD
BLACK LCAQUER
TRIM

$45

MIDWEST

M32
CA1936
WOOD

$200

MIDWEST

CA1936
WOOD

$200

MIDWEST

M36
CA1936
WOOD

$350

MISCELLANEOUS

850

CA1947
IVORY
PLASKON

$60

1250

CA1948
BAKELITE
BED-RADIO

$75

387

CA1938
IVORY
PLASKON
METAL TRIM

$225

'LULLABYE'

CA1941
BAKELITE
BED-RADIO

$90

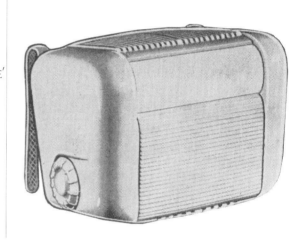

510

CA1951
PLASTIC

$45

'LUMITONE'

CA1941
BAKELITE
LAMP-RADIO

$225

MODERNAIRE

CA1948
RED
PLASTIC
(ONE TUBE)

$250

MONARCH

CA1936
WOOD
BLACK LACQUER
DETAIL

$150

MONARCH

CA1934
WOOD
2-TONE
LACQUER

$50

MONARCH

'LIBERTY'
CA1935
WOOD
2-TONE
LACQUER
STATUE OF
LIBERTY DIAL

$175

MONARCH

CA1935
WOOD
BLACK LACQUER
TRIM

$125

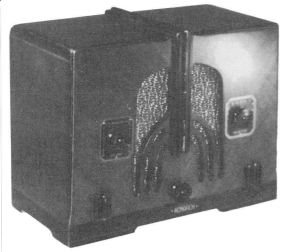

NORTHERN
ELECTRIC

5400
'BABY
CHAMP'
CA1948
BAKELITE
W/PLASKON
TRIM

$70

NORTHERN ELECTRIC

5000
'RAINBOW'
CA1947
BAKELITE

$150

OLYMPIC

7-421-V
CA1948
BAKELITE

$75

OLSON

CA1948
PLASTIC

$60

OLYMPIC

449
CA1949
PLASKON

$75

OLYMPIC

6-502
CA1948
WOOD

$65

PACIFIC BELL

CA1948
WOOD

$100

PACKARD-
BELL

CA1948
BAKELITE

$50

PACKARD-
BELL

45
CA1935
WOOD

$250

PACKARD-
BELL

5FP
CA1946
IVORY
PLASKON

$75

PACKARD-
BELL

551
CA1948
WOOD
BAKELITE GRILLE

$45

PACKARD-
BELL

35
CA1935
WOOD

$225

PHILIPS
(CANADA)

B1C12U
CA1959
PLASTIC
(PASTEL COLORS)

$75

PHILIPS (CANADA)

B1C13U
CA1959
PLASTIC
(PASTEL COLORS)

$75

PLA-PAL

'POKERADIO'
CA1934
WOOD
BLACK LACQUER & CHROME TRIM
(SIDES OPEN FOR LIQUOR, SHOT-GLASSES, TOP OPENS FOR CARDS, CHIPS)

$400+

PHOENIX

CA1935
WOOD
2-TONE LACQUER

$50

PLA-PAL

'PYRAMID'
CA1934
WOOD

$150

PLA-PAL

CA1935
WOOD
2-TONE LACQUER

$100

PREMIERE

CA1934
WOOD
2-TONE LACQUER

$60

PREMIERE

527
CA1938
WOOD

$70

PURITAN

G418
CA1948
METAL

$60

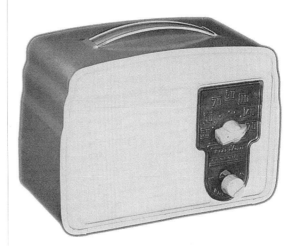

PROMONETTE

CA1948
SWIRLED
PLASTIC

$125

RADIOLAMP
OF AMERICA

CA1933
BRASS
LAMP-RADIO

$350

PURITAN

CA1946
BAKELITE

$80

RADIOLETTE

CA1935
WOOD

$50

RADOLEK

325
CA1940
WOOD

$40

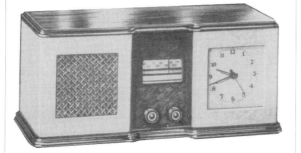

RADOLEK

C17544
CA1940
WOOD

$60

RADOLEK

C17522
CA1940
WOOD

$75

REMLER

'SCOTTY'
CA1940
IVORY
PLASKON

$250

RADOLEK

C17543
CA1940
WOOD

$65

REMLER

'SCOTTY'
CA1947
BAKELITE

$150

REMLER

5
'SCOTTY'
CA1941
IVORY
PLASKON

$150

SHARP

PF116
CA1948
WOOD
BLACK LACQUER
W/HAND-
PAINTED SCENE
(OCCUPIED
JAPAN)

$125

REMLER

26-110
'SCOTTY'
CA1936
BAKELITE
W/PLASKON
TRIM

$350+

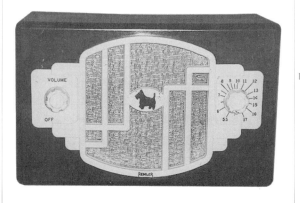

SILVER

CA1937
WOOD
BLACK LACQUER
TRIM

$200

RETS

CA1948
BAKELITE

$45

SILVER

CA1940
PAINTED POT
METAL

$125

MISCELLANEOUS

43P
CA1934
WOOD
BLACK LACQUER
GRILLE

$100

SPM

CA1935
ETCHED
MIRROR

$1000+

SIMPLEX

CA1934
WOOD

$90

STERLING

'DELUXE'
CA1950
PLASTIC WITH
ETCHED
METAL TOP

$150

SIMPLEX

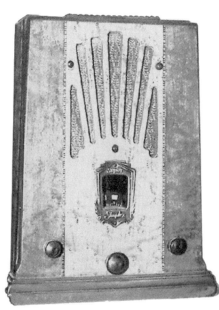

CA1934
WOOD
MARQUETRY

$150

SUPERTONE

CA1936
WOOD
MARQUETRY
BLACK LACQUER
TRIM

$150

SUPERHET

CA1938
BAKELITE

$75

TOSHIBA

CA1938
WOOD
W/BAKELITE
FRONT

$200

TEMPO
TONE

CA1937
WOOD
BRASS &
TENITE TRIM

$500+

TROUBADOR

'BULLET'
CA1940
BAKELITE

$100

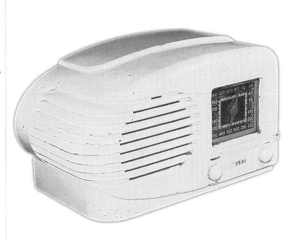

TOM
THUMB

3526S
CA1948
SWIRLED
PLASTIC

$110

TROY

CA1933
WOOD
MINI-
TOMBSTONE

$125

Miscellaneous

CA1935
BLUE
MIRROR

$1000+

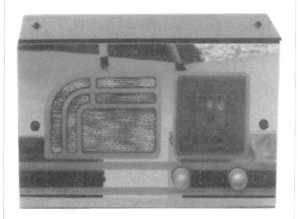

327
CA1938
WOOD

$125

CA1948
BAKELITE

$100

4048
CA1933
WOOD
MARQUETRY

$80

306
CA1938
WOOD

$100

CA1936
WOOD

$135

UNKNOWN

CA1935
WOOD

$150

UNKNOWN

CA1936
WOOD

$60

UNKNOWN

CA1935
ETCHED
MIRROR

$1000+

UNKNOWN

CA1936
WOOD

$200

UNKNOWN

CA1935
ETCHED
MIRROR

$1000+

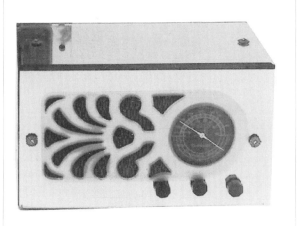

UNKNOWN

CA1936
WOOD

$175

MISCELLANEOUS

CA1937
WOOD

$75

CA1947
PAPIER
MACHE
DOG

$250

CA1937
WOOD

$150

CA1939
BAKELITE

$125

CA1939
WOOD

$75

12D
CA1937
WOOD

$60

WELLS
GARDNER

5D2
CA1937
BAKELITE

$125

WINGS

CA1935
WOOD
MARQUETRY

$175

WESTERN

CA1936
WOOD

$60

ZEPHYR

CA1937
WOOD
CHROME TRIM

$275

WESTERN
AIR PATROL

CA1940
BAKELITE

$75

NOTES